A-c Motor-control Fundamentals

A machine tool control panel. (*Square D Company.*)

A-c Motor-control Fundamentals

R. L. McINTYRE

Training Director, Joint Apprenticeship and Training Committee
for the Electrical Contracting Industry, Houston, Texas

McGRAW-HILL BOOK COMPANY, INC.

NEW YORK   TORONTO   LONDON

1960

A-C MOTOR-CONTROL FUNDAMENTALS

Library of Congress Catalog Card No. 59-15056

45105

Preface

The purpose of this book is to present the technical subject of motor controls and their application in language as non-technical as possible. The book is designed for use as a text in apprentice and industrial training programs and courses in technical, vocational, and trade schools; it should also be useful to technicians, servicemen, and others for self-study and reference.

To make use of this text, the reader needs a working knowledge of basic electrical theory; but the mathematics requirement has been kept to a minimum. Where new terms are used for the first time, they are fully explained. Most texts on this subject approach control circuits from the standpoint of memorizing basic circuits, which leaves the student handicapped because of the endless variations in circuits in actual practice. This text shows how to develop circuits step by step to perform any desired function. In order to build a background for circuit development, the text presents a discussion of the possible functions of control and the components used in control circuits. The sections on components discuss the general construction and operation of each type rather than any one manufacturer's product.

The subject of motors and their characteristics has been well presented in several other books; therefore only a limited amount of material on motors as such has been included. There are sections devoted to maintenance and trouble-shooting of controls and, finally, an introduction to static control. A detailed study of three systems of static control is covered, along with the appropriate symbols and circuit diagrams.

The beginning student should study the material in the order in which it is presented. The sections preceding circuit development are necessary in order to apply the technique used. It is recommended that the student supplement his study of components with catalogs published by the various component manufacturers. This will give him a broad understanding of the different applications of the principles. While studying the section on circuit analysis, the student should obtain additional circuits, preferably for equipment he is familiar with, and practice the principles set forth in the text. Each chapter is followed by a brief summary and a set of study questions as instructional aids.

The book presents a system of study, application, and analysis of control circuits which has been applied by the author with gratifying results both on the job and in class for the past fifteen years.

R. L. McINTYRE

Contents

$\mathcal{S}$ignalite

APPLICATION NEWS

A General Instrument company

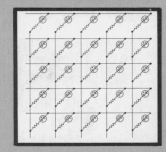

Vol. 7, No. 3

MULTILAYER BOARD CHECKER

By: Donald R. Dupree
George C. Marshall Space Flight Center
National Aeronautics and Space Admin.

Many electronic circuit packages, especially aerospace, now use multilayer printed circuit boards to accomplish the interconnection and routing of signals. These boards are comprised of layers of printed circuits ($\approx$.004") which are laminated together and interconnected by plated through holes.

In a particular application at Marshall Space Flight Center, Huntsville, Alabama, a digital differential analyzer was to be fabricated utilizing the multilayer boards technology. As a result, a method of testing was needed which would yield a reliable product at a reasonable expense, since the total number of boards needed was small.

The major requirements for the testing system were:
1. To insure that each conductor was routed properly to the correct points.
2. To insure that stray nets resulting from foreign particles, material flaws, etc., and improper etching, etc., do not exist.

Also in this issue . . .
DIAGNOSING A COMPUTER WITH NEONS, see page 340

Figure 1   Figure 2

To accomplish these objectives, a test fixture was designed using neon lights. The fixture (Figures 1 and 2) consisted of 691 neon lights; one for each separate connection on the multilayered board. If one attempted to check these points with a continuity checker from each point to every other point, it would take 239,086 separate measurements.

$$\leqq = \frac{X\ (X-1)}{2}$$

Using the neon light method, and depending on the circuit routing, one measurement may check a number of points so the number of operations necessary for checking one board was only about 125. The testing time for a board, which would hold 45 integrated circuits, was about 4 man-hours.

Holding fixture for multilayer board checker

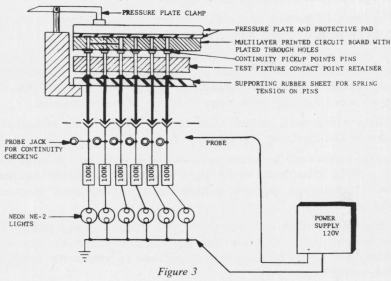

Figure 3

Multilayer Printed Circuit Board continuity checker. When voltage is applied to probe points, all points common to probed point will light the bulbs. This indicates that circuit lines within the multilayer board are connected and are making contact to all points specified by drawings.

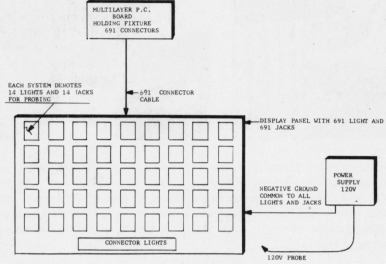

Figure 4

A holding fixture (See Figure 3) was constructed with press pickups at each plated through hole which corresponds to each lead on the then to be mounted integrated flatpacs.

From each pickup, a wire was routed through a resistor to a terminal and to a light. These lights were grouped to correspond with the flatpacs on the multilayer board.

The neon bulbs had one side common and connected to one side of a 120V power supply (See Figure 4).

To check a circuit or net, the other terminal of the 120V supply was connected to the terminal at the neon light, which provided a closed circuit through the multilayer board, and through the interconnect wires lighting each neon to which it was connected.

Points which were connected to each other could be identified by observing the lights on the panel.

Points connected by error were easily recognized. It was found that a NE2 neon bulb would light with a 3 megohms resistance between connectors so even a high resistance incorrect connection would be found.

Neon bulbs used as indicators also have an advantage over incandescent bulbs, because the current is limited by the series resistor, and is not of sufficient magnitude to stress the multilayer board connections.

DIAGNOSING A COMPUTER WITH NEONS

By: Charles N. Thompson, Jr.
Federal Aviation Administration

Because many people seem to attribute near-human qualities to computers, it is sometimes difficult to remember that these are simply machines (albiet complex ones) and, as such, are totally logical in their behavior. Realization of this fact makes diagnosis of various troubles and the status of various sections easily accomplished using simple circuitry and neon lamps.

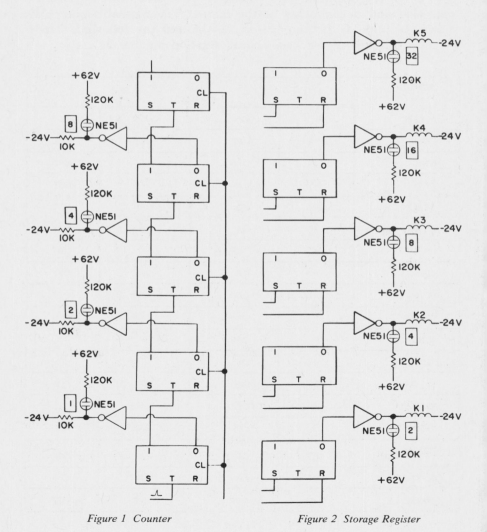

Figure 1 Counter   Figure 2 Storage Register

With the low speed computer at our facility we use neon lamps to indicate:

(1) data in counters
(2) malfunction of a counter
(3) data in the storage register
(4) state of the storage register relays.

The data in the counter is determined by means of the circuit shown in Figure 1, and is simply the sum of the numbers adjacent to the ionized lamps. For example, assume the lamps numbered 1 and 4 are glowing. This means that the data in the counter are 5.

To check the operation of the counter we observe the sequence of ionization and de-ionization of the lamps. The normal sequence is shown in Table I. If lamp 2 remains lit and the following lamps remain extinguished, we then suspect flip-flop number 2.

NUMBER OF INPUT PULSES	LAMPS			
	#1	#2	#4	#8
ZERO	OFF	OFF	OFF	OFF
ONE	ON	OFF	OFF	OFF
TWO	OFF	ON	OFF	OFF
THREE	ON	ON	OFF	OFF
FOUR	OFF	OFF	ON	OFF
FIVE	ON	OFF	ON	OFF
SIX	OFF	ON	ON	OFF
SEVEN	ON	ON	ON	OFF
EIGHT	OFF	OFF	OFF	ON
NINE	ON	OFF	OFF	ON
TEN	OFF	ON	OFF	ON
ELEVEN	ON	ON	OFF	ON
TWELVE	OFF	OFF	ON	ON
THIRTEEN	ON	OFF	ON	ON
FOUR-TEEN	OFF	ON	ON	ON
FIFTEEN	ON	ON	ON	ON
SIXTEEN	OFF	OFF	OFF	OFF

Table I

The number of bits stored in the Storage Register are determined by the circuit shown in Figure 2. In this circuit we add the numbers of the unlit lamps to obtain the necessary information. All lamps are lit with no bits in storage. If the lamps numbered 4, 8, and 16 are not glowing, we can determine the number of bits by adding 4 plus 8 plus 16 which equals 28 bits.

The lamp drivers (inverters) are combined ten to a printed circuit board. The schematic of one inverter with its lamp is shown in Figure 3. The nominal input voltage is from zero to minus twelve volts from the flip-flop. The transistor is cut off with 0 volts input.

Assume at turn-on that zero volts remains at the input. This applies about 86 volts across the neon lamp, and the lamp ionizes. When the input level changes to minus twelve volts the transistor is forward biased and is conducting heavily. The potential at the

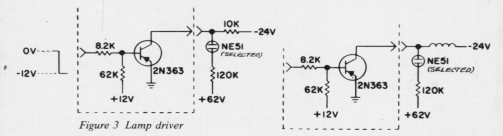

Figure 3 Lamp driver

Figure 4 Lamp and relay driver

junction of the selected NE51 lamp the 10K resistor is less than one volt above ground potential. When this occurs the voltage across the lamp is below the minimum required to maintain ionization and the lamp, therefore, extinguishes.

Figure 4 shown the inverter with the lamp and relay. In this circuit the lamp is glowing and the relay is de-energized when the transistor is cut off. When the transistor turns on, the relay energizes and the lamp ceases glowing.

These neon lamps are a great aid in rapidly diagnosing our computer when it malfunctions as well as giving us status information at any given time.

It is Signalite's policy to publish letters based on their intrinsic interest only. We do not necessarily agree with all comments and suggested uses and will upon occasion wait for your reaction before taking editorial space for ours.

BINGO!

Dear Sir:

Here is sort of an odd ball use of neon glow lamps. I have been building these things for years for church and other organizations where they are legal. Of course I have improved on them thru the years.

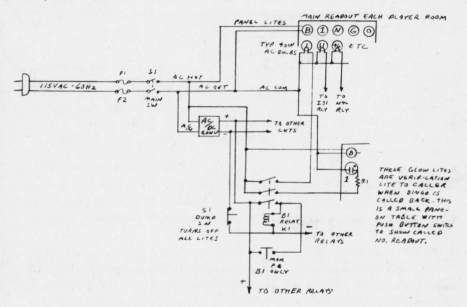

To pay off, Bingo must be mechanized and yet simple enough for everyone to keep up. Basically you need a light display in each calling room, and the caller can't see any of the big displays normally. To keep DC and building cost to a minimum, the alpha-numerical glow lamps are on a panel with the push buttons. As he calls a number, he punches this button, which in turn lights all room displays and the glow lamp. After the Bingo read back, which he checks against the glow lamps, he punches the dump button turning all lights out.

Yours very truly,

Robert C. Burks
Hughes Aircraft Company

HASN'T MISSED A BLINK

Dear Sir:

   We use your neon bulbs exclusively in all of our power supplies (we build our own), but the use I am going to describe is mainly for attention. I built a circuit to be semi-perpetual to draw attention to a "no smoking" sign.

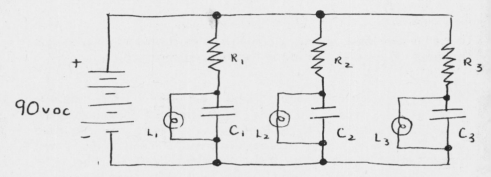

   So far this circuit has run continuously for 2 years without any circuit components being replaced. The neon bulbs haven't missed a blink, and the battery is still going strong.

Charles De Shon

Mid-Continent Lab.

THE THIRD WIRE THEME

Gentlemen:

   In our line-operated equipment we have standardized on three-wire operation and we often find that our customers do not have three-wire systems in their place of business. We therefore supply a three-wire adapter to them. Inevitably they call us to find out what to do with the third wire and how do they know they have hooked it up properly.

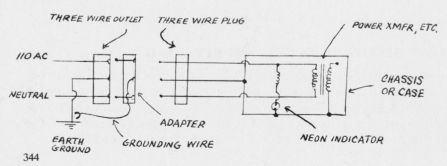

For the past two years we have included the following simple wiring procedure such that the neon pilot light will also serve as an indicator of correct grounding procedure. The lamp will not operate unless the equipment *is* grounded and *properly* grounded.

Yours truly,

W. H. Wandell, Jr.
The Vicon Instrument Company

(Ed. Note:

This same basic approach can also be used on a two-wire system to check for polarity as shown in the following letter.)

This circuit is useful with portable equipment in which one side of the AC line is connected to the chassis when the equipment is on. To avoid electrical shock to the operator of the device and/or to avoid blown fuses the AC plug is plugged into the receptacle with the "Power Switch" in the OFF position. If the neon bulb lights, the plug is in-

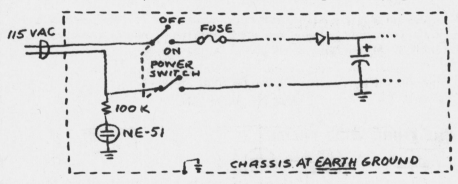

correctly polarized in the AC receptacle and will have to be reversed. If the bulb does not light when the AC plug is plugged into the receptacle, polarization is OK and it is safe to turn on the device. It is assumed that one leg of the AC line is at ground potential.

D. T. Walker, P. E.

RELAY SEQUENCE OPERATION REVISITED

(Ed. Note: In our last issue we published Mr. James Laino's circuit and description for determining the opening sequence of a relay's contacts. Several readers, including Mr. Laino himself, have written to point out that the circuit as shown would not perform the function claimed. The following letter, which shows the corrected circuit, is typical.)

Dear Mr. McKendry:

By this time you are probably aware that Mr. James E. Laino's circuit for indicating the first of multiple relay contacts to "open", as indicated on Page 335 of *Signalite Application News (Vol. 7, No. 2)*,

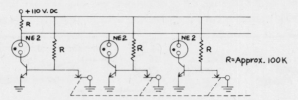

will not work because the circuit associated with each relay contact is completely independent (except for a common voltage supply).

For proper operation, all neon bulbs should be supplied through a common resistor as shown in the schematic diagram, below.

Respectfully submitted,

Louis F. Mayle

Magnavox Consumer Electronics Co.

NEON LAMP HOWLER

Gentlemen:

This is an audio frequency oscillator, whose supply voltage is modulated by another slow relaxation oscillator. It is essential that

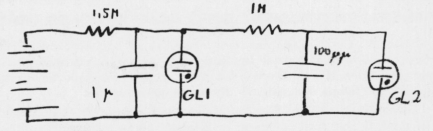

the ignition voltage of GL2 is appreciably lower than that of GL1.

Yours truly,

Joseph Braunbeck
Western Germany

SENSES INCOMING AC SIGNALS

Gentlemen:

(Below) is a drawing of a different use of a neon glow lamp. We are presently manufacturing a device which needed to sense incoming

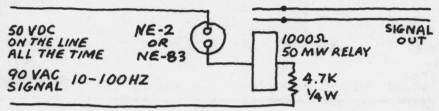

AC signals of about 90 VAC between 10 - 100 Hz. At the same time, there is approximately 50 DC standing on the signal pair.

As you can see this is definitely a job for a neon glow lamp.

Thank you,

Eric P. Yeasel
Cyco Electronics

Ed. Note:

If lamps are used which have a low maintaining voltage, once ignited they will stay on. To avoid this a lamp with a maintaining voltage rating in excess of 50 volts should be used.

GENERAL INSTRUMENT EOPG ADDS ANOTHER UNIT

Alvin W. Gershon, Group Vice President of the Electro-Optical Products Group of General Instrument Corporation, has announced the acquisition of Nore Electric Co., Ltd., manufacturers of miniature automotive lamps and gaseous discharge noise sources.

The addition of Nore Electric, located in Southend-On-Sea, Essex, England, is the third company in England to be acquired, and the fifth member of the recently formed EOPG. Headquarters for the group is in Neptune, New Jersey.

"The product lines of Nore are ideally suited for inclusion in the Group," Mr. Gershon noted. "The miniature automotive lamps complement the product line of Vitality Bulbs in England which we acquired recently. The gaseous discharge noise sources and solid state noise generators complement the lines produced by Signalite here in the United States."

The other members of the Electro-Optical Products Group are Chicago Miniature Lamp Works, Chicago, Ill., Hivac, Ltd., England, Vitality Bulbs, Ltd., England, and Signalite Inc., Neptune, N.J.

Drop Us A Line. . . .

If you have an interesting application of neon glow lamps in your circuitry. . . or a problem concerning the use of neon lamps, drop us a note telling about it. Interesting letters will be published in a future issue of the **Application News**—and we will send you an Owl Eye Nite Lite for your home.

Applications which in the opinion of Signalite have significant interest will also be brought to the attention of the editors of leading technical publications for consideration as articles and featurettes. If you would like help in preparing your material for publication, just send us the facts and data. We will put it in the correct form for publication. Your by-line and company credit will be given with your permission.

For immediate technical application or circuit design assistance, you may contact Signalite directly at:

TWX: 201-775-2255   *TEL: 201-775-2490*

* * * * *

For information about Signalite Neon Glow Lamps for circuit component and/or indicator applications, for specifications on lamps, for general information about Signalite and its products, call us at any of the following telephone numbers:

Phoenix, Arizona	(602) 254-6085	Neptune, New Jersey	(201) 775-2490
Anaheim, Calif.	(714) 828-1344	Albuquerque, N. Mex.	(505) 255-1638
Los Altos, Calif.	(415) 948-7771	Poughkeepsie, New York	(914) 471-1623
Los Angeles, Calif.	(213) 274-8485	Rochester, New York	(716) 889-1429
Denver, Colorado	(303) 388-4391	Syracuse (Liverpool), N.Y.	(315) 472-7886
Tampa, Fla.	(305) 422-3460	Utica, New York	(315) 736-9195
Chicago, Illinois	(312) 777-2250	Charlotte, No. Car.	(704) 375-8958
Fort Wayne, Indiana	(219) 743-4411	Cincinnati, Ohio	(513) 521-2290
Indianapolis, Indiana	(317) 359-5374	Cleveland, Ohio	(216) 333-2585
Louisville, Kentucky	(502) 893-7303	Dayton, Ohio	(513) 298-9546
Baltimore, Maryland	(301) 484-3647	Pittsburgh, Penna.	(412) 242-0100
Benton Harbor, Mich.	(616) 927-2041	Dallas, Texas	(214) 528-6286
Southfield, Mich.	(313) 358-2020	Houston, Texas	(713) 468-0232
St. Paul, Minn.	(612) 488-7293	Salt Lake City, Utah	(801) 466-8709
St. Louis, Missouri	(314) 727-6123	Scarborough, Ont. Can.	(416) 751-5980
Kansas City, Missouri	(816) 763-3634	St. Laurent, Que., Can.	(514) 331-4884

Printed in U S

1

Fundamentals
of Control

Since the advent of mass production, the machine has become a vital part of our economy. In the beginning machines were operated chiefly by hand and powered from a common line shaft. This line shaft was driven by a large motor that ran continuously and was connected to the individual machine by a belt when needed. It should not be hard to see that this type of power did not lend itself to quantity production.

With the demand for more and more production, the machine took on a new look. Down came the line shaft, and the electric motor went into the individual machine. This change allowed more frequent and more rapid starts, stops, and reversals of the machine. A small machine could have a small high-speed motor, while next to it a large machine could have a large constant- or variable-speed motor. In other words, the machine shop or factory became more flexible. Once the drive motor was put on the machine, with the sole function of operating one piece of equipment, it was possible to introduce some automatic operations.

Today in our industrial plants, more and more machines are being made fully automatic. The operator merely sets up the original process, and most or all operations are carried out automatically. The automatic operation of a machine is wholly dependent upon motor and machine control. Sometimes this control is entirely electrical and sometimes a combination of electrical and mechanical control is used. The same basic principles apply, however.

A modern machine consists of three separate divisions which need to be considered. First is the machine itself, which is designed to do a specific job or type of job. Second is the motor, which is selected according to the requirements of the machine as to load, duty cycle, and type of operation. Third, and of chief concern in this book, is the control system. The control-system design is dictated by the operating requirements of the motor and the machine. If the machine needs only to start, run for some time, and stop, then the only control needed would be a simple toggle switch. If, however, the machine needs to start, perform several automatic operations, stop for a few seconds, and then repeat the cycle, it will require several integrated units of control.

It is the intent of this book to present the basic principles and components of control and then show how they are put together to make a control system.

1-1 Meaning of Control

"What is motor control?" This is a question that has no simple answer. It is not, however, the mysterious, complicated subject that some people believe it to be.

The word *control* means to govern or regulate, so it must follow that when we speak of motor or machine control, we are talking about governing or regulating the functions of a motor or a machine. Applied to motors, controls perform several functions, such as starting, acceleration, speed, power, protection, reversing, and stopping.

Any piece of equipment used to regulate or govern the functions of a machine or motor is called a *control component.*

Each component will be taken up in a separate chapter of this book.

An *electric controller* is a device or group of devices that controls or regulates the functions of a motor or machine in a predetermined manner or sequence.

1-2 Manual Control

A *manual controller* is one having its operations controlled or performed by hand (Fig. 1-1). Perhaps the most popular single type in this category is the manual full-voltage motor

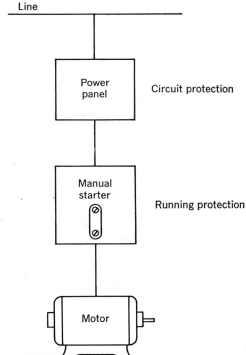

Fig. 1-1 Manual control for a motor.

starter in the smaller sizes. This starter is used frequently where the only control function needed is to start and stop the motor. Probably the chief reason for the popularity of this unit is the fact that its cost is only about one-half that of an equivalent magnetic starter. The manual starter generally gives overload protection (Sec. 2-7) and low-voltage release (Sec. 2-12), but does not give low-voltage protection.

Manual control which provides the same functions as those achieved by the manual full-voltage motor starter can be had by the use of a switch with fusing of the delayed-action type, which will provide overload protection for the motor.

Examples of this type of control are very common in small metalworking and woodworking shops, which use small drill presses and lathes and pipe-threading machines. Another good example is the exhaust fan generally found in machine shops and other industrial operations. In this installation the operator or maintenance man generally pushes the start button for the fan in the morning when the plant opens, and it continues to run throughout the day. In the evening, or when the plant is shut down, the operator then pushes the stop button, and the fan shuts down until needed again. The welding machines of the motor-generator type are a very common example of this kind of control and should be familiar to most students of motor control.

The compensator, or manual reduced-voltage starter, is used extensively to control polyphase squirrel-cage motors where reduced-voltage starting is required and the only control functions required are start and stop. The compensator gives overload protection, low voltage release, and low-voltage protection. The compensator type of starter is quite frequently used in conjunction with a drum controller on wound-rotor motors (Fig. 1-2). This combination gives full manual control of start, stop, speed, and direction of rotation.

The compensator, being a reduced-voltage starter, is generally found only on the larger horsepower motors. A very common use for the compensator with the addition of a drum controller is found in the operation of many centrifugal-type air conditioning compressors. The reduced-voltage feature is used to enable the motor to overcome the inertia of the compressor during starting without undue current loads on the system. The drum controller, through its ability to regulate speed of a wound-rotor motor, provides a means of varying the

capacity of the air conditioning system, thus giving a flexibility that would not be possible with a constant-speed full-
voltage installation.

These are just a few of the manual controllers, but you
should have little trouble classifying any unit of this type be-

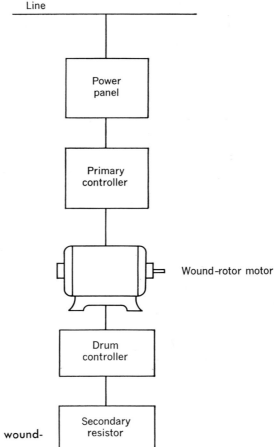

Fig. 1-2 Control for wound-
rotor motor.

cause it has no automatic functions of control. Manual control is characterized by the fact that the operator must move a
switch or push a button to initiate any change in the condition
of operation of the machine or equipment in question.

1-3   Semiautomatic Control

Controllers that fall in this classification use a magnetic starter and one or more manual pilot devices such as push buttons, toggle switches, drum switches, and similar equipment (Fig. 1-3).   Probably the most used of these is the push-button station because it is a compact and relatively inexpen-

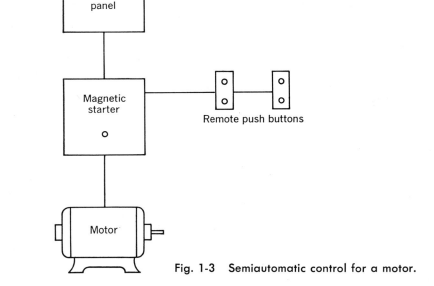

Fig. 1-3   Semiautomatic control for a motor.

sive unit.   Semiautomatic control is used mainly to give flexibility of control position to installations where manual control would otherwise be impractical.

The key to classification as a semiautomatic control system lies in the fact that all the pilot devices are manually operated and that the motor starter is the magnetic type.   There are probably more machines operated by semiautomatic control than by either manual or automatic. This type of control requires the operator to initiate any change in the attitude or operating condition of the machine. Through the use of the magnetic starter, however, this change may be initiated from any convenient location, as contrasted to the manual controls requirement that the control point be at the starter.

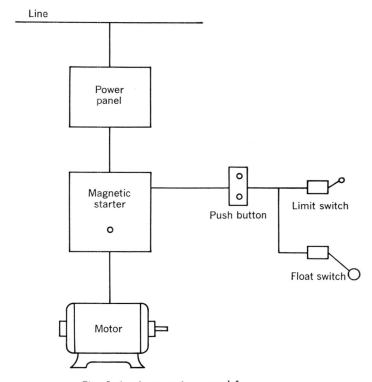

Fig. 1-4 Automatic control for a motor.

1-4 Automatic Control

An automatic controller is a magnetic starter or contactor whose functions are controlled by one or more automatic pilot devices (Fig. 1-4). The initial start may be automatic, but usually it is a manual operation, activated by a push-button station or switch.

In some cases there may be a combination of manual and

automatic pilot devices in a control circuit.   If the circuit contains one or more automatic devices, it would be classed as an automatic control.   Consider, for example, a tank that must be kept filled with water between definite limits and a pump to replace the water as it is needed.   If we equip the pump motor with a manual starter, and station a man at the pump to turn it on and off as needed, then we would have manual control.   Now let's replace the manual starter with a magnetic starter and put a push-button station at the foreman's desk. If we rig a bell to let him know when the water is low and again when it is high, he can do other work and just push the proper button when the bell rings.   This would be semiautomatic control.   Now suppose we install a float switch that will close the circuit when the water reaches a predetermined low level and open it when it reaches a predetermined high level.   When the water gets low, the float switch will close the circuit and start the motor.   The motor will now run until the water reaches the high level, at which time the float switch will open the circuit and stop the motor.   This would be automatic control.

Even though the automatic system would cost more to install than the other two, it requires no attention by an operator, thus saving the cost of his labor.   This may well make it the cheapest method to use.   The automatic control would be more accurate because there is no delay between the water reaching the desired level and the closing or opening of the control circuit.

Automatic control systems are to be found in almost all machine-tool installations.   Tools such as drill presses, milling machines, shapers, turret lathes, precision grinders, and almost any other type of machine in common use may, through the use of limit switches and other automatic pilot devices, perform their operations more efficiently and rapidly by the use of automatic control systems.

SUMMARY

The basic difference in manual, semiautomatic, and automatic control lies in the flexibility of the system.   With manual control the operator must go to the physical location of the starter to make any change in the operation of the machine. With semiautomatic control the operator may have his control point at any convenient location so that he might initiate changes in the operation from the most desirable position. With automatic control the necessity of the operator initiating the necessary changes has been eliminated for each automatic operation that is included in the control system.

2

Control
of Motor Starting

Control circuits and equipment can perform varied functions. These can be grouped into 11 general types according to the effect they have on the motor to be controlled. Each of the general types can be broken down into endless variations, but they each stem from a few basic principles which, if understood, are the key to control work. It is the aim of this chapter to present these principles in as nontechnical a language as possible.

2-1 Motor Starting

There are several general factors to be considered in the selection of motor-starting equipment. The most obvious of these are the current, voltage, and frequency of the motor and control circuits. Motors require protection according to the type of service, the type of motor, and the control functions that will be needed.

Whether to use a full-voltage starter or a reduced-voltage starter may depend on the current-carrying capacity of the plant wiring and the power company lines and rates. Other factors, such as the need for jogging or inching, acceleration control, or the type of motor to be used, will also affect this selection.

Full-voltage Starting. The requirement of this type of starting is simply that the motor leads and line leads be connected (Fig. 2-1). This could be accomplished merely by

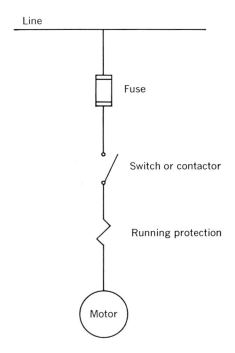

Line

Fuse

Switch or contactor

Running protection

Motor

Fig. 2-1 Full-voltage starting.

using a knifeblade switch, but this method would provide no protection for the motor except the circuit fusing.

For small fractional-horsepower motors on low-amperage circuits, the simple switch may be satisfactory and is used frequently. Many appliances use nothing more than the cord and plug as the disconnecting means, with a small toggle switch to start and stop the motor. Because the motor is not disconnected from the line on power failure, this type of starting control can be an advantage for fans and other devices that otherwise would have to be restarted.

For motors up to 7½ horsepower and not over 600 volts, the manual across-the-line motor starter may be used to give manual control. Most of these units give overload and under-voltage protection.

The most popular starters for motors up to 600 horsepower and 600 volts or less is the magnetic across-the-line starter. This starter, combined with pilot devices, can give full protection to the motor and fully automatic operation.

The vast majority of motors today are built to withstand the surge of current that occurs when they are suddenly thrown across the line. Not all our plant circuits can stand this surge, however, nor can all the power company equipment. When a large motor starts at full voltage, it may cause a voltage drop large enough to drop out other control equipment. Should the voltage drop be serious enough, it might even cause a dimming of lights in other buildings.

In most industrial installations the utility company penalizes, in the form of higher rates, for surges of excessive current on the line by the use of a demand meter. The demand meter registers the maximum average demand of power on the line for a given period of time, generally a 15-minute period. This factor should always be taken into consideration when the method of starting large motors is being decided. The extra cost of power because of the excessive demand for starting large motors across the line may well exceed the cost of reduced voltage starting, which would materially reduce the demand reading.

When considering using full-voltage starting, always check the building wiring and distribution system capacity. Should the wiring be inadequate, either it must be increased in capacity or reduced-voltage starting must be used.

Reduced-voltage Starting. Whenever the starting of a motor at full voltage would cause serious voltage dips on the power company lines or the plant wiring, reduced-voltage starting becomes almost a necessity (Fig. 2-2). There are, however, other reasons for using this type of control. The effect on the equipment must be taken into account in the selection of motor starters. When a large motor is started across the line, it puts a tremendous strain or shock on such things as gears, fan blades, pulleys, and couplings. Where the load is heavy and it is hard to bring it up to speed, reduced-voltage starting may be necessary. Belt drives on heavy loads are apt to have excessive slippage unless the torque is applied slowly and evenly until full speed is reached.

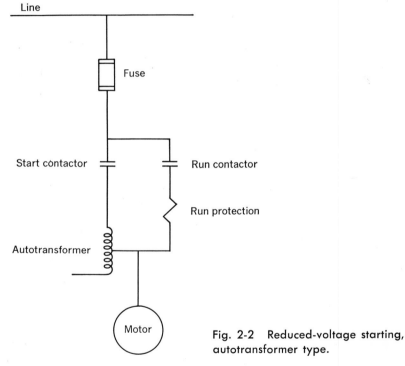

Fig. 2-2   Reduced-voltage starting, autotransformer type.

Reduced-voltage starting is accomplished by the use of resistors, autotransformers, or reactors in order to reduce the line voltage to the desired value during starting. Regardless of the means of reducing the voltage, it must be designed to fit the particular motor to be started. It is not within the scope of this book to go into the design of reduced-voltage starters, but rather to point out the need for proper selection according to the specifications furnished by the motor manufacturer.

Another method of achieving reduced-voltage starting is to use a wound-rotor motor with secondary control (Fig. 1-2). With this system, a full-voltage starter is used on the primary or stator winding, and resistance grids are put in series with the secondary or rotor winding to reduce torque and starting current. The secondary control device shorts out the resistance grids as needed for acceleration, until at full speed all the resistance is shorted out and the motor runs as a squirrel-cage motor. The advantage of secondary control is that it gives speed control as well as reducing the starting current.

Regardless of the method used to provide reduced-voltage starting, it must be kept in mind that the starting torque of the motor is also reduced. If a motor is not capable of starting its load under across-the-line conditions, the application of reduced-voltage starting will only aggravate the situation because of the reduced starting torque. The torque of an induction motor is a function of the square of the rotor current, or approximately the square of its line current. If the starting voltage is reduced to 50 per cent, the motor current will be reduced to 50 per cent of normal, but the torque will be reduced to 25 per cent of normal.

Some of the methods of obtaining reduced-voltage starting will result in very little or no acceleration under starting conditions. This requires that the total acceleration occur after full voltage has been applied. The starting current during reduced-voltage conditions will be somewhat less than across-the-line starting current. When full voltage is applied, however, the starting current will be approximately the same as it would have been if the motor had been placed across the line in the beginning. This type of starting is generally referred to as *increment starting* and is used generally to spread the rate of change of current demanded from the line over a longer period of time. Part-winding squirrel-cage motor starting and wye-delta starting of squirrel-cage motors generally fall in the increment-start category.

Jogging and Inching. Printing presses, cranes, hoists, and similar equipment require that the motor be started repeatedly for short periods of time in order to bring some part of the

machine into a given position. This process is known as *jogging*
or *inching*. Even though these terms are often used inter-
changeably, there is a slight difference in their meaning. If
the motor is started with full power in short jabs, it is jogging.
If the motor is started at reduced speed so as to let the machine
creep to the desired spot, then it is inching.

When jogging service is required, the starter must be derated. For instance, a size 3 starter rated at 30-horsepower
220-volt three-phase normal duty should be derated to 20
horsepower for jogging duty. The manufacturer's literature
should be consulted for ratings of starters in jogging service.

2-2   Acceleration Control

Squirrel-cage motors do not generally lend themselves very
well to speed or acceleration control. There are special types
of squirrel-cage motors designed for two-, three-, or four-speed
applications. This type of multispeed squirrel-cage motor
does not have a true variable speed but rather has several
definite speeds which may be used as desired or in steps. When
adjustable speed is required, the wound-rotor motor with secondary control or the adjustable-speed a-c commutator motor
is probably the most practical.

Manual control of acceleration or speed may be accomplished
with multispeed squirrel-cage motors by having the operator
close the proper contactor as determined by the load or speed
requirements. With wound-rotor motors, the secondary or
drum controller is advanced as needed to give the desired speed.

Automatic control of acceleration may be accomplished by
several methods. Probably the simplest is *definite time control*. With this method, a time-delay relay is used for each
step or speed. When the motor is started in its lowest speed,
the first time-delay relay is energized. When this relay times
out, it energizes the second contactor, increasing the speed to
its second step. This process may be carried through as many
steps as necessary to give the speed and acceleration desired.
The chief disadvantage of this method is that it is not affected
by the conditions of the machine, its load, or the motor current.

For machines or equipment that cannot stand full torque

until the load has reached a given speed, the system called *current-limit control* should be used to accelerate the motor. In this system each step is brought in by a current relay which will not close the circuit for its speed until the current has dropped to a safe value. The current, of course, will not drop until the motor and the load are running at nearly the same speed. This system is very well suited for belt or gear drives with heavy high-inertia loads. This method of control must be designed for the particular application, and the relays must be set for the particular machine and its requirements. For this reason, they are not available as standard stock controllers.

Another system of acceleration control is *slip-frequency control*. This system is used on wound-rotor motors and is also used to energize the field of synchronous motors.

Because the secondary voltage and frequency of wound-rotor motors is proportional to the speed, a frequency-sensitive relay may be used to energize each progressive step or speed. One disadvantage to slip-frequency control is that it must be started on a first, or lowest, speed.

The following features must be kept in mind when selecting the method of acceleration control for a motor: Manual control is sensitive only to the operator's reaction. Definite time control is sensitive only to the lapse of time. Current-limit control is sensitive to the load on the motor. Slip-frequency control is sensitive to the speed of the motor.

It is quite possible that under certain specific applications a combination of any two or more of the above-mentioned control systems might be used to enable the motor to be sensitive to more than one of these factors. Such a controller would of necessity be custom-built to meet the specific requirements of a given installation.

2-3   Starting Squirrel-cage Motors

Single-speed squirrel-cage motors are generally started by the use of across-the-line magnetic starters. A multispeed squirrel-cage motor, however, requires a controller that is built for its particular windings.

Two-speed motors may either have two separate stator windings (Fig. 2-3), or be of the consequent-pole type, which have only one stator winding. The two speeds are obtained with the consequent-pole motor by regrouping the coils to give a different number of effective poles in the stator. It is characteristic of this type of motor that it gives a two-to-one speed ratio. Three-speed motors usually have one winding for one speed and a second winding that is regrouped to give the other

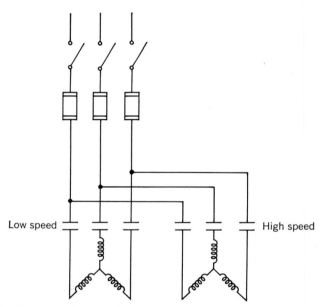

Low speed   High speed

Fig. 2-3   Two-speed squirrel-cage motor with separate stator windings and controller.

two speeds. Four-speed motors usually are wound with two windings which are regrouped to give two speeds each. The number of contactors, the order in which they close, and the number and types of overload units required depend on the method of obtaining the various speeds.

2-4   Starting Wound-rotor Motors

The wound-rotor motor is essentially the same as a squirrel-cage motor except that it has definite windings instead of short-circuited bars on the rotor. By the introduction of resistance into the rotor windings, with a drum controller or with contactors, the speed may be controlled in any number of steps. The most common method of starting wound-rotor motors is by the use of a manual or magnetic full-voltage starter on the primary, interlocked to the secondary controller (Fig. 2-4).

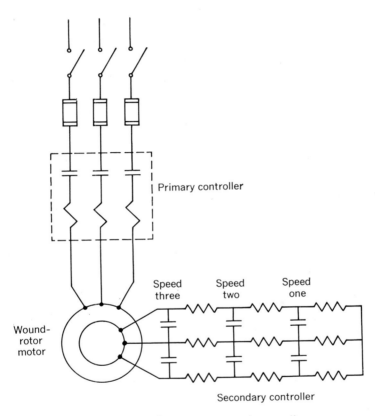

Fig. 2-4   Wound-rotor motor and controller.

The secondary controller may be a manual drum controller, a motor-driven drum controller, a liquid rheostat, or a magnetic contactor designed for secondary control. The secondary controller may be for starting service only and have only two or three steps, or it may be for speed control as well and have any number of steps.

It is necessary that there be an interlock between the primary and secondary controllers that will prevent the motor from starting unless all the resistance is in the secondary circuit.

The secondary circuit may use either a resistance, a reactance, or an autotransformer for control. These will be taken up in detail in a later chapter.

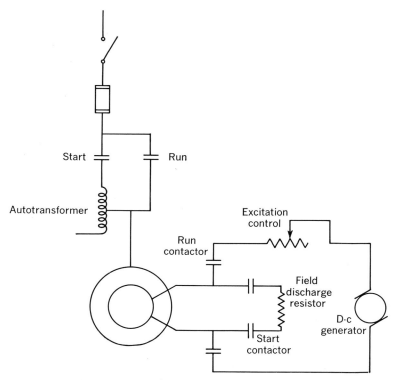

Fig. 2-5   Synchronous motor and controller.

2-5   Starting Synchronous Motors

The synchronous motor starts as a squirrel-cage motor with a resistor connected across the field winding to dissipate the current generated in this winding (Fig. 2-5). Usually the stator controller is a reduced-voltage starter with the addition of a slip-frequency or field-application relay to apply d-c voltage to the rotor at about 95 per cent of synchronous speed. The slip-frequency relay must also remove field excitation and connect the field resistor if the motor should pull out of step. If the excitation is not removed, the stator winding will be subject to damaging current. The synchronous motor should be provided with an incomplete-sequence relay to protect the starting winding if the starting sequence should not be completed. Provision must be also made to adjust the field excitation.

While the above description of the starting of a squirrel-cage motor may seem to be oversimplified, it is intended to be general in nature and to apply to all synchronous motors. For a specific application of a definite type of synchronous motor, the manufacturer's literature on the individual motor should be consulted. Many synchronous motors are designed for specific applications and vary somewhat from this general outline for starting in that they require additional steps or equipment.

2-6 Selection of Starting Controllers

There are several points that must be considered when selecting starting controllers. Listed below are some questions that should be asked whenever selection of a controller is necessary:

1. Is it designed for the type of motor to be used?
2. Does the motor require reduced-voltage starting?
3. Is speed control needed?
4. Does the controller offer all the types of protection that will be needed?
5. Are the line and control voltages and frequency correct?

Analyze the needs of the machine and the motor before selecting any controller, and avoid costly mistakes.

2-7 Overload Protection

Overload of a motor may be mechanical or electrical in origin; therefore, the overload protection must be sensitive to either. The current that a motor draws from the line is proportional to the load on the motor, so if this current is used to activate the overload protection device, the machine as well as the motor will be protected.

Overload protection is achieved in almost all controllers by placing a heating element in series with at least two motor leads on multiphase motors (Fig. 2-6). These heater elements activate electrical contacts, which open the coil circuit when used on magnetic controllers. When used on manual starters or controllers, the heating elements release a mechanical trip to drop out the line contacts.

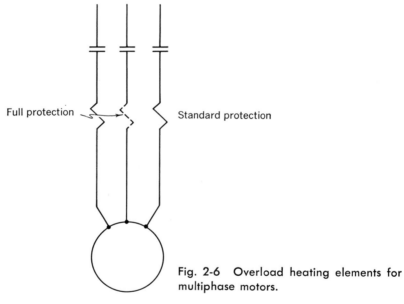

Full protection   Standard protection

Fig. 2-6 Overload heating elements for multiphase motors.

The overload relay is sensitive to the percentage of overload, so that a small overload will take some time to trip the relay, whereas a heavy overload will cause an almost instantaneous opening of the circuit. The overload relay does not give short-circuit protection, however. It is quite possible that under short-circuit conditions the relay might hold long enough to allow considerable damage to the motor and other equipment.

It would be impossible to overstress the necessity of proper selection of overload protective equipment. The manufacturer's rating of running current for a specific motor should be adhered to in the selection of the heating elements for overload relays. The all too frequent practice of increasing the size or rating of the heater element beyond the value called for is probably the greatest single cause of motor failure in industrial plants today. When a motor is tripping its overload units, a careful check of the actual current drawn should be made in order to determine whether the fault lies in the overload protective device or in the motor itself actually drawing excessive current. Should the motor be found to be drawing excessive current, then it must be determined whether this is caused by mechanical overload or by defective windings within the motor itself. Many times, today's heavy production schedules require that the operator demand more from his machine than its motor is capable of producing. The practice of increasing the allowable current through the overload units will only hasten the time when a shutdown of the equipment is necessary in order to rewind or replace the motor.

When one phase of a motor circuit fails, the motor is subject to what is commonly called *single phasing*. This condition causes an excessive current to flow in the remaining motor windings and leads. In most cases, this excessive current will cause the overload units to trip, thus disconnecting the motor from the line and preventing a burnout of its windings. Under certain particular conditions of load characteristic of the individual motor, it is possible for the motor to run single phase and burn out its windings, even though there are two overload units in the control device. For this reason, many engineers and architects are specifying the third overload unit to give a better degree of phase-failure protection.

2-8   Short-circuit Protection

Squirrel-cage and other a-c motors may draw up to 600 per cent of full load current under severe starting loads. Any load over this amount is considered short-circuit current. Since the overload relay is designed to pass these large currents for a short period of time, they cannot give short-circuit protection. The circuit feeding a motor must have either a fused disconnect or a circuit breaker ahead of the motor to give short-circuit protection. The design of fuses is such that they will open the circuit much faster than the overload relays under short-circuit conditions. Probably, the best protection is given with the dual-element type of fuse, or circuit breaker.

The dual-element fuse (Fig. 2-7) is so constructed that one of its elements consists of a fuse link. This link will open very rapidly under short-circuit conditions. The second element in this type of fuse consists of a thermal element which has considerable time lag in the process of breaking the circuit. The net result of using the dual-element fuse on motor circuits is to give short-circuit protection through the fuse link and yet a degree of overload protection in the thermal element. This

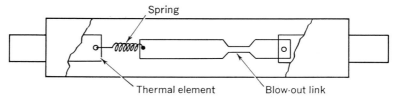

Spring

Thermal element   Blow-out link

Fig. 2-7   Dual-element cartridge-type fuse.

type of fuse is used extensively as the only means of protection on small fractional-horsepower motors.

The use of a circuit breaker for short-circuit protection offers a degree of time lag for starting loads in that breakers are inherently a thermal device and require some time lag in order to open. This time lag is inversely proportional to the amount of current. The larger the overload, the shorter the time required to open the circuit.

2-9   Limit Protection

Limit protection, as its name implies, must limit some function of the machine or its driving motor. The most common type of limit control is used to limit the travel of a cutting tool or table or other part of a machine tool. When the cutter reaches a predetermined setting, it will activate a limit switch, causing the motor to reverse and the machine to return to the

other extreme of travel.   There are other types of limit protection, such as limits for over- or underspeed of the driven machine.   There are also limit controls which do not reactivate
the machinery at all but merely stop the motor until corrections
have been made by the operator.

This type of protection is accomplished by the use of limit
switches, which will be discussed fully later.   Basically, a limit

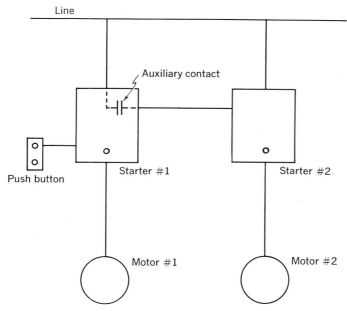

Fig. 2-8   Two motor starters interlocked so that motor no. 1 must run
first and automatically starts motor no. 2.

switch is merely a switch with a mechanical bumper or arm
that will allow some action of the machine to throw the switch
mechanism.   Limit switches are one of the most frequently
used control devices on machines today.

2-10   Interlocking Control

Interlocking is preventing one motor from running until
some other motor or sequence has been activated.   A good
example of this is found in air conditioning.   If the compressor

were to run without the cooling-tower pump running, the compressor-head pressure would rise dangerously, and either the high-limit pressure switch would shut the machine down or the compressor would be damaged. To prevent this from occurring, the compressor should be interlocked to the pump so that it cannot start until the pump is running.

Interlocking may be electrical or mechanical or a combination of both. Reversing starters built with both starters in the same box generally have a mechanical interlock and sometimes have an electrical interlock. When the two units to be interlocked are in two separate boxes (Fig. 2-8), then electrical interlocking is a necessity. Electrical interlocking is accomplished by connecting an auxiliary contact on one starter in series with the coil circuit of the second starter.

While we have discussed interlocking only in relation to motors, it is well to realize that interlocking is used in all phases of control wiring whether it is involved in the starting of a motor or in the closing of valves in a process-control installation. The use of interlocking control assures the proper sequence of operation for the entire control system.

2-11   Speed Control

Squirrel-cage motors do not lend themselves to any system of continually variable speed control, but rather may be had in two, three, or four speeds according to the design of the motor. These were discussed under acceleration control. The most versatile a-c motor as far as speed control is concerned is the wound-rotor motor, sometimes referred to as a *slip-ring* motor. By the use of secondary control, this type of motor can have as many steps of speed as are desirable. Methods of controlling wound-rotor motors will be discussed more fully when we take up their controllers.

Another type of a-c motor which gives excellent speed control is the a-c commutator type of motor.

There are four general types of speed control, depending on the requirements of the machine:

Constant Speed. Many machines require only a reduced speed for starting and then a constant speed for operation.

This type of speed control may be accomplished by using a reduced-voltage starter on either a squirrel-cage, wound-rotor, or synchronous motor. It must be kept in mind, however, that reduced-voltage starting also invariably gives reduced starting torque.

Variable Speed. Variable speed is a requirement that a motor must operate at several different speeds at the selection of the operator. This type of control may best be accomplished by the use of a wound-rotor motor with a secondary controller or a commutator-type a-c motor. This type of control requires that a speed change be made under load.

Multispeed Control. This type of control differs only slightly from variable-speed control in that it usually does not require speed changes under load. The multispeed squirrel-cage motor is well suited for this type of service.

Predetermined Speed Control. With this type of control, the machine is accelerated through the necessary steps of speed to a preset operating speed. Both multispeed squirrel-cage and wound-rotor motors are suitable for this type of service.

Compelling Sequence Control. Any of the above types of speed control may be wired so that the operator may vary the sequence of operation. Quite frequently, however, the control system compels the operator to start at a particular place in the sequence and follow it through without variation. When the control is of this type, it is known as *compelling sequence control.* This term applies to control systems other than speed control and is dependent only on the requirement that it compels the operator to follow a set sequence of operation.

2-12 Undervoltage Protection and Release

The line voltage supplying motor circuits may drop to dangerously low values or may be shut off at almost any time. When the voltage is too low, severe damage may be done to the motor windings if they are allowed to remain on the line. While some large motors employ a special voltage relay to disconnect the motor under low-voltage conditions, most smaller motors depend on the overload units to open the starter contacts.

If the control circuit is such that the motor will restart when the power is restored to its proper value, the protection is referred to as *undervoltage release*. The use of maintained-contact pilot devices on magnetic starters gives this type of protection.

If the protection used requires that the motor be restarted manually, then the protection is referred to as *undervoltage protection*. The use of momentary-contact pilot devices on magnetic starters gives this type of protection.

Whether to use undervoltage protection or undervoltage release depends upon the requirements of the machine. Ventilating fans, unit heaters, and many other small units in a plant may operate more effectively with undervoltage release. This saves the necessity of having to restart them. In any machine where there is the slightest risk that the machine or operator might be injured by an unexpected start, undervoltage protection should by all means be used.

2-13   Phase-failure Protection

When a three-phase motor has the current interrupted on one phase, this condition is referred to as *single phasing*. Ordinarily the overload units will trip the starter and remove the motor from the line. There is, however, a condition of loading for each motor where it may quite possibly burn up without causing excessive current to flow through the overload units. This is generally about 65 per cent of load for most squirrel-cage motors. For small motors the risk is generally considered too slight to warrant the cost of additional protection. For large motors a voltage relay is placed across each phase, and its contacts are connected in series with the holding coil of the starter. Failure of one phase will drop the starter out at once.

The use of three overload relay units on the starter gives what is generally considered adequate phase-failure protection for most motor installations up to 100 horsepower.

2-14   Reverse-phase Protection

Some machines could be severely damaged when the motor runs in reverse, as would occur with a reversal of phasing. While this is not a common type of protection, when it is needed, it can prevent costly damage.

Reverse-phase protection can be accomplished by the use of a phase-sensitive relay with its contacts in series with the holding coil of the starter.

2-15   Incomplete Sequence Protection

When reduced-voltage starting is used on a motor, there is a danger that the motor windings or the autotransformer or both might be damaged through prolonged operation at reduced voltage.   To prevent this condition and to assure the completion of the starting cycle, a thermal relay is placed across the line during starting.   This relay is so designed and connected that prolonged starting will cause the thermal unit on the relay to open its contacts and drop out the starter.   This type of protection is also necessary on synchronous motor controllers.

Another method of obtaining incomplete sequence protection for starting of motors is by the use of the timing relay which will disconnect the motor if it has not completed its starting sequence in the predetermined length of time.

2-16   Stopping the Motor

There are several factors that must be considered in stopping a motor.   On some machines all that is necessary is to break the motor leads and let the motor coast to rest.   Not all machines can be allowed to coast, however.   For instance, a crane or hoist not only must stop quickly, but also must hold heavy loads.   Other machines, such as thread grinders, must stop very abruptly, but need not hold a load.

The method of stopping may be either manual or automatic.   Automatic stopping is accomplished by the use of limit switches, float switches, or other automatic pilot devices.

Manual stopping is controlled by push buttons, switches, or other manually operated pilot devices.

The most common method of stopping is merely to remove the motor from the line by breaking the circuit to the starter coil, if it is a magnetic starter, or by tripping the contacts of a manual starter with the stop button.

For motors that must be stopped very quickly and accurately but which do not need to hold a load, probably the most widely used method is known as *plugging*. This is accomplished by

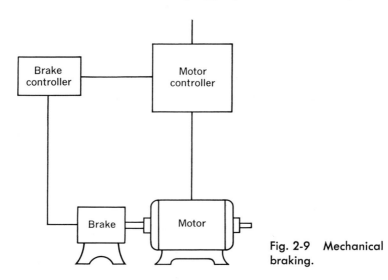

Fig. 2-9   Mechanical braking.

the use of an automatic plugging switch or a plugging push button in conjunction with a reversing starter.

With either of these units, the motor starter is dropped out and then momentarily energized in the reverse direction. The momentary reversal plugs the motor to an abrupt stop. This type of stopping will not do for cranes or hoists because it will not hold a load.

When dealing with equipment such as cranes and hoists, we must consider that the load has a tendency to turn the motor. This is known as an *overhauling* load. When a-c motors are used they frequently are of the wound-rotor type and stopping is preceded by a slowing of the motor through one or more steps. This slowing helps to nullify the over-hauling load. As the motor is dropped from the line, a mechanical brake (Fig. 2-9) is automatically applied which locks the motor shaft connected to the load.

When d-c motors are used, the overhauling load is slowed down by the use of dynamic or regenerative braking, then a friction brake is applied.

Synchronous motors are sometimes stopped by the use of dynamic braking. This is acomplished by removing the line from the motor and placing a resistance across the motor leads, thus making an a-c generator out of the motor. The resistor presents a heavy load to the generator, causing it to come to a rapid stop. Care must be taken to use a resistor unit capable of dissipating the power generated while stopping the motor. It must also be noted that this type of stop cannot be used for frequent stopping because the resistor units must have time to cool between operations.

SUMMARY

A student beginning the study of motor control may feel that he will never learn all the functions that might be performed in the control of a motor or other device, and well he might. The advances made in this field are so rapid and far-reaching that new ones are developed almost daily. When analyzed completely, however, most of them are merely variations of the basic functions set forth in this chapter. It must be kept in mind that intelligent servicing, development, or installation of control equipment depends upon a thorough understanding of the requirements of the machine and the characteristics of the motor.

REVIEW QUESTIONS

1. What is motor control?
2. What are the three basic types of motor control?
3. Name the two types of starting control.
4. How many types of protection are there for motors?
5. Do the running conditions of the motor affect the type of control to be used on a motor?

6. What is the difference between an automatic and a semiautomatic controller?

7. What factors need to be considered when selecting starting equipment?

8. What are the two basic methods of reduced-voltage starting?

9. How can the acceleration of motors be controlled automatically?

10. Reversing starters must be equipped with some form of _____ to prevent both starters from closing at the same time.

11. When the motor is momentarily reversed to bring it to a stop, the function is called _____.

12. Is the time it takes the overload relay to drop out the starter affected by the percentage of overload?

13. What is the difference between overload and short-circuit protection?

14. What is incomplete sequence protection and on what two types of motors would it most likely be used?

3

Control Components

As soon as it has been decided what functions of control are needed for a machine, the components or devices to perform these functions must be selected. This selection should be made with care. For instance, if a float switch is needed and its duty cycle is only a few operations per day for a year or so, one of the cheaper competitive units might be satisfactory. If, however, the duty cycle is a few hundred operations per day on a permanent basis, then the best-quality unit available should be used. The small savings gained through the use of cheap components are usually soon offset by costly shutdowns due to failure of the components to function properly. In this chapter each of the basic types of control components will be discussed, how it works, both electrically and mechanically, and at least some of the functions that it can perform.

The student is strongly urged to obtain manufacturers' catalogs on control components as a further reference for use with this chapter. The more familiar the student becomes with the various manufacturers' equipment and the way it operates, the better prepared he will be to service it on the job.

3-1 Switches and Breakers

The one component common to all but the very smallest motors is a switch or breaker for disconnecting the motor. There are two types of switches in general use on motor circuits. The first of these is the isolation switch, which is rated only in voltage and amperes. This type of switch has no interruption capacity rating and must not be opened under load. Quite often the switch used for this purpose is a nonfused type.

The second type of switch is a motor-circuit switch, which is capable of interrupting the motor current under normal overloads. This type of switch is rated in horsepower and, when used within this rating, is capable of being used as a starting switch for motors (Sec. 2-1). When used for disconnecting and motor-circuit protection, this switch must be of the fused type.

Circuit breakers offer the same disconnecting features as switches and the circuit protection of fuses. The breaker operates on a thermal-released latch so that it may be reset and used again after an overload. Being built all in one unit and offering short-circuit protection, as well as serving for disconnecting, makes this unit more compact than a switch and fuse combination.

Switches and breakers may perform the functions of start (Sec. 2-1), stop (Sec. 2-16), overload protection (Sec. 2-7), and short-circuit protection (Sec. 2-8), depending upon their rating and use in the circuit.

3-2 Contactors

The contactor itself is not generally found alone in motor-control circuits. It is, however, the basic unit upon which the motor starter is built. Contactors are used to perform the functions of start and stop on many heavy loads such as electric furnaces, signs, and similar types of equipment that do not require running protection.

Perhaps the best way to describe a contactor would be to say that it is a magnetically closed switch. It consists of one set of stationary contacts and one set of movable contacts which are brought together by means of the pull of an electromagnet. The vast majority of contactors use an electromagnet and contact arrangement that falls into one of two general types. The first of these is the clapper type (Fig. 3-1). The contacts are fastened to the pole pieces of the magnet and hinged so that they swing more or less horizontally to meet the stationary contacts.

The second is the solenoid type (Fig. 3-2). On this contactor the contacts are mounted on the upper end of the core

Fig. 3-1   Clapper-type contactor. (*Square D Company.*)

of a magnetic solenoid. When the electromagnet is energized, the core is pulled up into the solenoid coil, thus lifting the contacts vertically to meet the stationary contacts mounted above the solenoid coil.

Regardless of whether the contactor is of the clapper or the solenoid type, the contacts themselves are broken by the pull of gravity when the electromagnet is deenergized.

All that is necessary electrically to operate the contactor is to provide a voltage of the proper value to the coil of the electromagnet. When the voltage is switched on, the contacts close, and when the voltage is switched off, the contacts open.

3-3   Relays

Automatic control circuits almost invariably contain one or more relays primarily because the relay lends flexibility to our control circuits.   The relay is by design a mechanical amplifier.

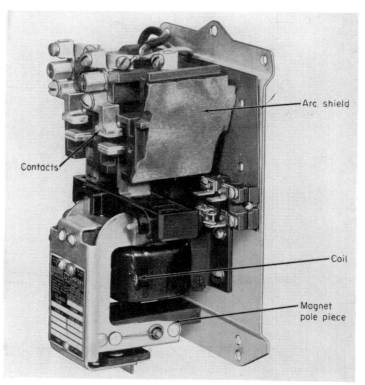

Arc shield

Contacts

Coil

Magnet pole piece

Fig. 3-2   Solenoid-type contactor. (*Square D Company.*)

Let us consider for a moment the meaning of the word *amplify*.   It means to enlarge, increase, expand, or extend. When we energize the coil of a relay with 24 volts and the contacts are controlling a circuit of 440 volts, we are amplifying the voltage through the use of a relay.   Relay coils require only a very low current in their operation and are used to control circuits of large currents. So again they amplify the current. The relay is inherently a single-input device in that it requires only a single voltage or current to activate its coil. Through the use of multiple contacts, however, the relay can be a multiple-output device which amplifies the number of operations controlled by the single input.

Suppose we have a relay whose coil operates on 110 volts at 1 ampere and the contacts of this relay control three separate

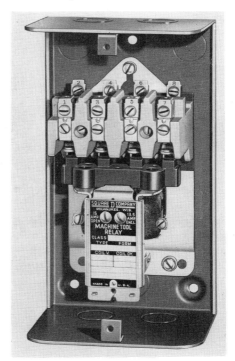

Fig. 3-3   Voltage relay.
(*Square D Company.*)

circuits operating at 440 volts and 15 amperes each. This relay then becomes a power amplifier in that it controls considerably more power in its output circuits than it consumes in its input circuit. It also becomes an amplifier in the terms of number of circuits as its single input controls three separate outputs.

Relays are generally used to accept information from some form of sensing device and convert it into the proper power

level, number of varied circuits, or other amplification factor
which will achieve the desired result in the control circuit.
These sensing devices used in conjunction with relays are commonly called *pilot devices* and are designed to sense or detect
such things as current, voltage, overload, frequency, and many
others, including temperature.   The proper type of relay to be
used in a given circuit will be determined by the type of sens-

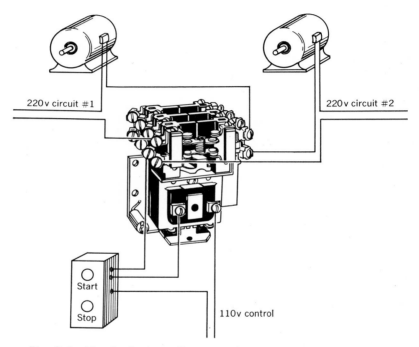

220v circuit #1

220v circuit #2

Start

Stop

110v control

Fig. 3-4   Circuit diagram illustrating basic use of voltage relays.

ing device which transmits the information to it.   For instance,
a voltage-sensing device must be connected to a voltage relay,
and a current-sensing device must activate a current relay.
Each of these types will be discussed individually.

Voltage Relay.   This type of relay (Fig. 3-3) is probably
the most common because it lends itself to so many applications
and can be used to perform so many functions.   The voltage
relay is merely a small contactor (Sec. 3-2) which opens or

closes its contacts, depending on whether they are normally closed or open whenever the proper voltage is applied to its coil. They are available with as many contacts either normally open or normally closed as needed. Voltage relays are used frequently to isolate two or more circuits controlled from one source (Fig. 3-4) or when the control voltage is different from line voltage.

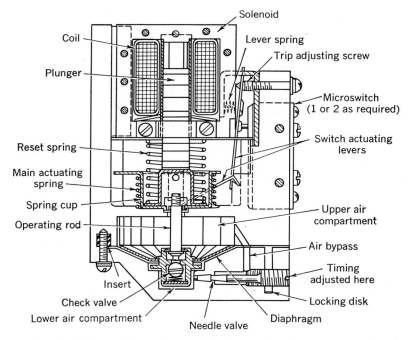

Fig. 3-5 Time-delay relay, air bleed type. (*Cutler-Hammer, Inc.*)

It must be remembered that while a voltage relay is not a primary control device, it does require a pilot device (Chap. 4) to operate it.

Current Relay. This type of relay (Figs. 3-6, 3-7, and 3-9) is used to open or close a circuit or circuits in response to current changes in another circuit, such as a current drawn by a motor (Sec. 2-1).

The current relay is designed so that when connected in

series with the circuit to be sensed, it will close after the current through its coil reaches a high enough value to produce the necessary magnetic flux. There are a few terms used in connection with current relays that must be understood.

Pull-in current is the amount of current through the relay coil necesary to close or pull in the relay.

Drop-out current is the value of current below which the relay will no longer remain closed after having been pulled in.

Differential is the difference in value of the pull-in and drop-out currents for the relay in question.

For example, if a relay is energized or pulled in at 5 amperes and drops out at 3 amperes, then the pull-in current is 5 amperes, the drop-out current is 3 amperes, and the differential is 2 amperes.

Most relays of this type are provided with spring tension and contact spacing adjustments which allow a reasonable variation of pull-in, drop-out, and differential values. This type of relay should not be operated too close to its pull-in or drop-out values unless it is provided with some form of positive throw device for its contacts. This is important because the amount of contact pressure depends upon the difference in actual current and pull-in current for the particular relay. For example, when the above relay is operated with only 5.01 amperes flowing through the coil, the contact pressure will be only that produced by the 0.01 ampere of current.

Generally, true current relays are used only on circuits of very low current. For heavier current applications, a current transformer is used and its output applied to either a current relay or a voltage relay with the proper coil voltage.

Another type of current relay is the thermal type, in which a bimetallic strip or other device is heated by a coil connected in series with the circuit to be sensed. The bimetallic type depends upon the difference in expansion of two dissimilar metals when heated. They are constructed by riveting together two thin strips of dissimilar metals. When the current in the circuit produces sufficient heat, the bimetallic strip expands and releases the contacts. Motor overload relays and fluorescent starters are examples of this type of relay.

Frequency Relay. The frequency relay is used to apply field excitation to synchronous motors (Sec. 2-5) and for acceleration control on wound-rotor motors. Most of these units are specially designed for a particular application. One type consists of two balanced coils arranged on a common armature. These coils compare a reference frequency with that of the sensed circuit. The relay is closed one way when the frequencies are the same, or within a predetermined percentage,

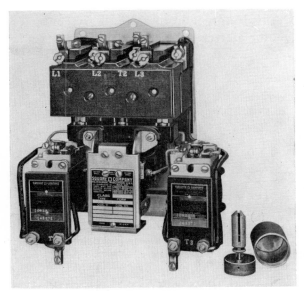

Fig. 3-6 Time-delay relay, dashpot type. Used as a current relay in overload service. (*Square D Company.*)

and is closed the other way when the frequencies differ by a given amount or more.

Time-delay Relay. This type of relay is often used for sequence control, low-voltage release, acceleration control, and many other functions.

Essentially, the time-delay relay is the voltage relay with the addition of an air bleed (Fig. 3-5) or a dashpot (Fig. 3-6) to slow down or delay the action of its contacts. This delay in action can be applied when the contacts are closing or when they are opening.

If the delay is to be applied when the contacts are closing, it is referred to as *time closing* (TC). If the delay is to be applied when the contacts are opening, then it is referred to as *time opening* (TO). Both types are provided with an adjustment so that the time delay can be set within the limits of the particular relay. These units are built in various sizes depending upon the contact rating needed.

Overload Relay. The overload relay is found on all motor starters in one form or another. In fact, the addition of some form of overload protection to an ordinary contactor converts it into a motor starter. This unit performs the function of

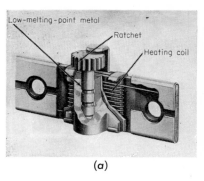
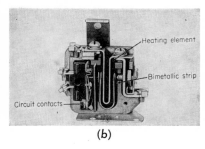

(a)   (b)

Fig. 3-7 Overload relays. (a) Low-melting-point metal type. (b) Bimetallic strip type. (*Square D Company.*)

overload protection (Sec. 2-7) and phase-failure protection (Sec. 2-13) in motor circuits. The basic requirement for overload protection is that the motor be allowed to carry its full rated load and yet prevent any prolonged or serious overload. When a motor is overloaded mechanically, motor current increases, which in turn increases the temperature of the motor and its windings. The same increases in current and temperature are caused by the loss of one phase on polyphase motors or a partial fault in the motor windings. Therefore, to give full overload protection, we need only to sense, or measure, the current drawn by the motor and break the circuit if this current exceeds the rated value for the motor.

There are two basic types of overload relays in general use

on across-the-line starters.   The first is a unit which employs
a low-melting-point metal to hold a ratchet (Fig. 3-7a), which
when released causes the opening of a set of contacts in the
coil circuit of the starter.   The second type uses a bimetallic
strip (Fig. 3-7b) to release the trip mechanism and open the
coil-circuit contacts.

Regardless of which type of device is used, it is activated by
a heating element placed in series with the motor circuit.   The

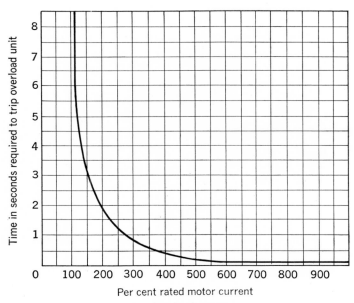

Fig. 3-8   Overload-relay current curve.

amount of current needed to cause the relay to trip is determined by the size of the heating element used.   When used for
protection of small motors drawing low current, a coil of small
wire or very thin metal is used as a heating element.   On larger
motors a heavier coil or strip of metal is used so that the same
amount of heat is produced when the rated amount of current
flows.   Thermal units used in overload relays have an inherent
time delay in their action that is inversely proportional to the
amount of overload.   This should be evident from a study of
the curve shown in Fig. 3-8.   When the overload is slight, the

motor can go on running for some time without tripping the overload unit. If the overload is great, however, the overload relay will trip almost at once, thus removing the power from the motor and preventing damage.

Thermal relays trip on heat and heat alone, and they cannot normally tell whether this heat is from the current to the motor or from the air that surrounds the starter. To offset this, it is sometimes necessary to install oversized heaters in high-temperature locations and undersized heaters in low-temperature

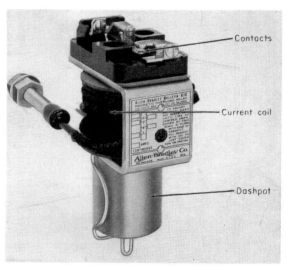

Fig. 3-9   Overload relay, magnetic type. (*Allen-Bradley Company.*)

locations. Some bimetallic units are designed to compensate for the ambient temperature change. This type of unit is called a *compensated overload relay.*

The third type of overload relay is magnetic (Fig. 3-9). This unit has a magnetic coil so connected that it senses the motor current either by the use of current transformers or by direct connection. When the current exceeds the rating of the motor, the overload coil lifts a plunger that forms its core and opens the contacts in the control circuit. Magnetic overload relays are generally found only on large motor starters.

Overload relays must be reset after each tripping either

automatically or manually. The automatic reset type should not be used except on equipment that is so designed, or used, that there can be no danger to life or equipment from the restarting of the motor. After the overload relay has been tripped, it requires a little time to cool, so that there is some delay before resetting can be accomplished.

3-4 Motor Starters

A motor starter in its simplest form consists of some means of connecting and disconnecting the motor leads from the line leads, plus overload protection for the motor. Many other refinements are added to this basic unit to achieve the desired degree of control and protection. There are many types and classifications of motor starters. Each of these types draws its name from the method or classification of operation of the motor that it starts. Some of these classifications are manual or automatic, full-voltage, reduced-voltage, single-phase or three-phase, and d-c or a-c. To describe a particular motor starter, it is necessary to use several of these terms or classifications. For instance, a particular motor might require a reduced-voltage, automatic, three-phase, a-c motor starter. Even this does not completely describe the unit, because it must be of a definite size for the motor and be rated for the proper voltage. Then we must know whether it is to be remotely controlled or to have a push button in the cover and many other features. In this chapter, we shall discuss many of these classifications, and the student should keep in mind that any particular starter might well be a combination of several of the types we discuss here.

Keep in mind that there is a difference between a motor starter and a motor controller. While it is difficult to draw a fine line between them, it is generally accepted that the starter consists of the means of connecting the motor to the line plus providing the protection needed. By contrast, a controller contains not only the motor starter but at least a major part of the sensing devices and relays necessary for the complete control system.

Motor starters are built to specifications approved by the

NEMA (National Electrical Manufacturers Association) standards. These standards include such things as sizes, so that a purchaser may expect the equipment to be built to handle its rated load. For instance, the size 0 starter in 440-volt three-phase service is rated at 3 horsepower. The size 1 starter is rated at 7½ horsepower, size 2 at 25 horsepower, size 3 at 50 horsepower, and size 4 at 100 horsepower. For lower voltage service, each size starter has a smaller horsepower rating because of the increased current demand by the motor running at a lower voltage.

Also included in the NEMA standards are types of enclosures for starters to satisfy code requirements for atmospheric conditions existing in the place of installation. NEMA type 1 enclosures are for general purpose use wherever atmospheric conditions are normal. They are intended primarily to prevent accidental contact with the control apparatus and energized circuits. NEMA type 3 enclosures are weather-resistant and protect against rain and sleet in outdoor applications. NEMA type 4 enclosures are watertight and suitable for outdoor applications on piers and in dairies and breweries. They may be washed down with a hose. NEMA type 7 enclosures are intended for use in hazardous gas locations such as are found in oil fields and satisfy the code requirements for class 1, group D, locations. NEMA type 8 enclosures are intended for gas locations where corrosive materials are present. This enclosure has oil-immersed contacts. NEMA type 9 enclosures are built for use in hazardous dust locations, whose code classification is class 2, groups F and G, such as flour mills. NEMA type 11 enclosures are for use as corrosion-free enclosures providing resistance to corrosion from both acid and fumes. Contacts are oil-immersed. NEMA type 12 enclosures are dust-tight industrial enclosures and are designed for use where enclosure is required to provide protection against dirt and oil.

If you were requested to order the starter for a 5-horsepower motor connected to a 220-volt three-phase line in ordinary service, you would need to specify several things. You would order a size 1 three-phase 220-volt across-the-line starter in a

NEMA type 1 enclosure. Additional information would be needed as to whether the starter should be manual or automatic, depending upon the type of control to be utilized in the installation.

3-5   Manual Motor Starters

To be classed as manual, a motor starter must depend upon the operator's closing the line contacts by pushing a button or moving a lever which is physically linked to the contacts in

Fig. 3-10   Manual motor starter.
(*Square D Company.*)

some manner. For an illustration, suppose we take the size 0 starter available in either manual or automatic type, having the push button in the cover. The manual type (Fig. 3-10) is so constructed that when the start button is pressed, a mechanical linkage forces the contacts to close. Once closed, the linkage is latched in this position. When the stop button is pressed, or the overload units open, the linkage is tripped and the contacts open.

By contrast, when the start button is pressed on the magnetic starter, it merely energizes the starter coil, which in turn magnetically closes the line contacts. The stop button or the overload relays break the circuit to the coil, thus allowing the line contacts to open.

The chief disadvantage of the manual starter is the utter lack of flexibility of control. It must be operated from the starter location, and it is definitely limited even as to protection-control possibilities. When the degree of control it offers is satisfactory for the installation, it does have the advantage of being less expensive. The vast majority of manual starters found in service will fall into one of three classes, namely, the thermal switch for use on very small single-phase motors, the size 0 and size 1 manual across-the-line starters in single- and three-phase motors, and the manual reduced-voltage compensator (Fig. 3-14) for large motors.

3-6   Automatic Motor Starters

The automatic starter, also known as a *magnetic starter,* depends upon the magnetic pull of an electromagnet to close and hold its line and auxiliary contacts. This type of starter offers unlimited flexibility of control. It is dependable and has a long life expectancy with reasonable maintenance. There are many mechanical arrangements used on this type of starter. They fall into two general classifications, however, depending on the movement of the magnetic coil core.

The first of these is the clapper type (Fig. 3-11a) which has the movable contacts attached to the hinge along with the magnetic core or a section of the core. The hinge is so arranged that the pull of the magnetic circuit swings the pole piece and the contacts in a more-or-less horizontal direction, and the stationary line contacts are mounted on the vertical backboard of the starter.

The second is the *solenoid* type (Fig. 3-11b). With this type, the operation is in the vertical direction. The contacts are mounted to the core so that when the core is pulled up into the coil, the movable contacts are raised to meet the stationary contacts mounted on a horizontal support at the top of the starter assembly.

Either of these basic types seems to be satisfactory, although each manufacturer has some reason for the particular type employed in his units. The larger starters generally use the clapper-type movement, but at least one company makes a complete line from size 0 through the largest with a solenoid-type action.

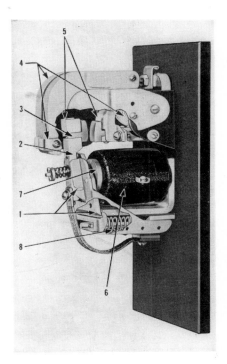

Fig. 3-11a Clapper-type construction as used for contactors and starters. 1. Hinge. 2. Contact arm. 3. Contact. 4. Arc shield. 5. Contact holders. 6. Coil. 7. Pole face. 8. Tension spring. (*Square D Company.*)

The all-important magnetic circuit consists generally of an adaptation of one of the three basic magnetic shapes (Fig. 3-12). The E or C type is used on most clapper-type starters, and the modified E or solenoid type is used on vertical-action starters.

When a-c coil circuits are used, the pole pieces of the magnet are equipped with a shading coil (Fig. 3-12*d*). This gives an out-of-phase flux to hold the contacts during the zero points of

current, thus preventing chatter of the contacts.   While this
method of preventing chatter is effective, many starters for
large motors employ a d-c coil circuit because of its constant
magnetic pull and freedom from any tendency to chatter.

Fig. 3-11b   Solenoid-type construction as used for motor starter and contactor. (*Square D Company.*)

There are also two basic types of contacts in general use.
Most small starters employ a bridge-type contact (Fig. 3-13).
The bridge-type contact offers good contact alignment and a
natural wiping action which helps to prolong contact life.
Most large starters employ the required number of spring-
mounted movable contacts that meet a corresponding number
of rigid stationary contacts (Fig. 3-11a).   The necessary wip-

ing action is obtained by making the contacts in a curved shape that allows them to slide into alignment as they close and open. This type of contact requires more maintenance to keep it in close alignment than does the bridge-type contact. Good contact alignment is necessary in order to prevent excessive arcing and contact pitting.

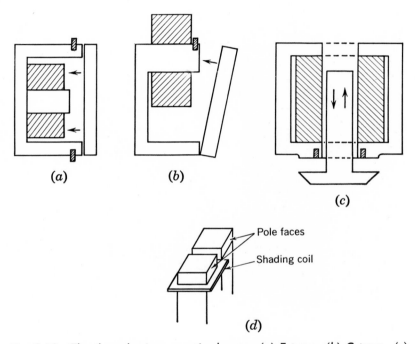

Fig. 3-12 The three basic magnetic shapes. (a) E type. (b) C type. (c) Solenoid type. (d) Magnetic pole piece showing shading coil.

The greatest single contribution to modern-day production machinery is the magnetic starter. The flexibility of control offered by the magnetic starter allows automation and automatic control accuracy never dreamed of, nor possible, with manual operation. This flexibility stems from the fact that all that is necessary to start a motor is to provide electric energy to the coil of the starter. The source of energy may be independent of the motor circuit and can be turned on and off from any point and by any means desired.

3-7 Full-voltage Starters

Full-voltage, or across-the-line, starters (Fig. 3-11*b*) are the most widely used type. They are used on almost all three-phase, squirrel-cage, and single-phase motors. This type of starter is also used extensively as primary control on wound-

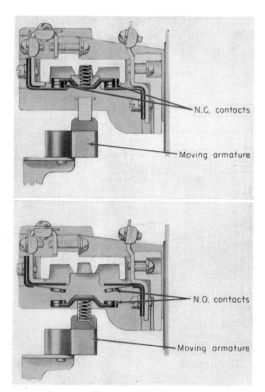

Fig. 3-13   Bridge-type contacts. (*Square D Company.*)

rotor motors that employ manual secondary control. Rated for use on motors up to 600 horsepower and up to 600 volts, they can give full protection to the motor, the machine, and the operator. The limitations on the use of this starter for squirrel-cage motors is only the strain imposed on the wiring system and the machine by the starting current and torque of the motor. Across-the-line starters are available in a variety of enclosures to meet the needs of starter location conditions. These enclosures conform to the standards published by the NEMA to suit every condition of location.   Availability also in either manual or magnetic types to suit the customer's needs adds to the flexibility of these units.

Fig. 3-14 Manual reduced-voltage starter, or compensator. (*Cutler-Hammer, Inc.*)

Any starter which connects the motor leads directly to the line voltage without any means of reducing the applied voltage or limiting the starting current would be classed as a full-voltage starter.

3-8 Reduced-voltage Starters

As the name implies, the reduced-voltage starter contains some means of reducing the line voltage as it is applied to the motor during the starting period. This is done in order to limit the inrush of current during the starting cycle. The requirements for using reduced-voltage starting depend upon several factors (Sec. 2-1). These units are built in either manual or automatic types, and, as with full-voltage starters, the manual type is cheaper but less flexible.

Manual reduced-voltage starters, more commonly referred

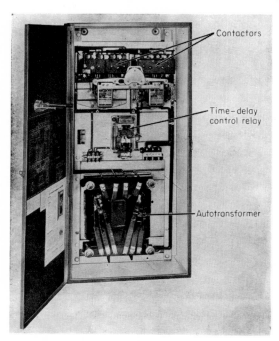

Fig. 3-15   Automatic reduced-voltage starter. (*Square D Company.*)

to as *compensators* (Fig. 3-14), consist of a double-throw switch and an autotransformer. The START position of the switch applies power to the motor through an autotransformer. The operating handle is held in this position until the motor is running at the highest speed it will attain, and full voltage is then applied by throwing the handle to the RUN position. The switch mechanism is held in the RUN position by a latch which can be released by either the undervoltage release, the overload units, or the hand trip. Generally, these units are in a self-contained metal enclosure that is designed to be wall-mounted.

Automatic reduced-voltage starters (Fig. 3-15) take many forms and are generally designed for a particular type of motor and for a particular application. The essential requirements are that some means be provided for connecting the motor to a source of reduced voltage and then automatically connecting it to the full line voltage after it has had time to accelerate.

The start contactor on a primary resistance starter need be

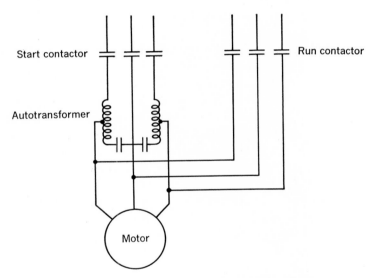

Fig. 3-16   Connections for starter autotransformer.

only a three-pole unit. This contactor connects the motor to the line in series with resistor units designed to limit the motor-starting current. The run contactor in this starter is also a three-pole unit which shorts out the resistors in order to apply full voltage to the motor.

The reactor type of reduced-voltage starter employs exactly the same contact arrangement as the primary resistance starter. The only difference in a starter for primary resistance and reactor type of reduced-voltage starting is in the use of reactors in place of the resistors.

The start contactor for an autotransformer type of reduced-voltage starter must be a five-pole contactor. The use of these five contacts is shown in Fig. 3-16. These contacts connect the motor to the line through the autotransformer connected open-delta. The run contactor in this starter consists of three contacts which apply full line voltage to the motor.

Regardless of its type, an automatic reduced-voltage starter must contain some means of automatically changing from START to RUN at the proper time. Generally, this is accomplished by the use of a time-delay relay (Sec. 3-3). In the case of primary resistance or reactance starters, this relay is required only to energize the coil of the run contactor. When used on an autotransformer starter, this relay must break the circuit to the start contactor and then make the circuit to the run contactor. The use of a time-delay relay in this service gives definite time control (Sec. 2-2). Another method which is sometimes used employs a form of current relay (Sec. 3-3) which will open the start contactor and close the run contactor when the motor current drops to a preset level. This gives current-limit control (Sec. 2-2).

When primary resistance or the reactor type of reduced-voltage starting is employed, there is no interruption of current to the motor. With the autotransformer type of reduced-voltage starting, however, the current is interrupted momentarily before the motor is placed across the line. When the current is not interrupted in the transition from reduced-voltage to full-voltage operation, it is referred to as a *closed-transition* start. When the motor is disconnected momentarily from the line and the current interrupted, it is referred to as an *open-transition* start. When the transition is of the open type, it is quite possible to have an inrush of current as high as twice the full-voltage starting current at the instant of voltage application. This surge of current is referred to as *transition current* and is the chief objection to the autotransformer type of reduced-voltage starting.

Any of these controllers may contain almost any or all of the protection control functions, such as undervoltage release

(Sec. 2-12), phase failure (Sec. 2-13), or incomplete sequence protection (Sec. 2-15).

One thing that you must keep in mind when choosing between manual and automatic controllers of this type is that when a manual unit is installed, it must be located so that the operator can not only see but also hear the motor, in order that he may properly judge when to apply full voltage. This limited selection of location can be overcome to some extent

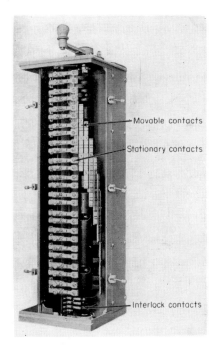

Fig. 3-17 Manual drum controller. (Cutler-Hammer, Inc.)

by installing a remote-indicating tachometer. This enables the operator to determine the degree of acceleration of the motor from the control location.

Another method of obtaining the effect of reduced-voltage starting is to use a wound-rotor motor with secondary control. This arrangement gives a higher starting torque with reduced starting current than does the squirrel-cage motor on primary reduced-voltage starting. The starter for such an arrangement would consist of an across-the-line starter connected to the primary of the motor.   The secondary, or rotor, winding of the motor is connected to resistance grids by means of either a manual or automatic drum controller (Fig. 3-17).   A second advantage to this arrrangement is that it can offer speed control as well as limited starting current.

3-9   Speed-control Starters

Besides the secondary speed control of wound-rotor motors, there are methods of controlling the speed of squirrel-cage motors, provided they are designed for multispeed operation.

One type of two-speed motor is wound with two separate stator windings and requires a starter with two sets of line contacts which can close only one set at a time.   This interlock (Sec. 2-10) may be either mechanical or electrical or both. Two separate across-the-line starters may be used with electrical interlock when a special unit is not available.   A reversing starter makes an excellent unit, provided the reverse phasing is eliminated.   The two sets of contacts or starters are wired so that each set connects one speed winding to the line.   As in other types of starters, they may be either manual or automatic.

Another type of two-speed motor is the consequent-pole motor, which has only one stator winding but gives two speeds by means of regrouping the stator coils to provide for a different number of poles.   While the dual-stator-winding motor might have almost any ratio of high to low speed, the consequent-pole motor gives a two-to-one speed ratio.   Three speeds may be obtained by using two stator windings.   One of these windings gives one speed, and the other is regrouped for a second and third speed.   To obtain four speeds, both windings must be regrouped.   To obtain multispeed and variable torque, the high-speed windings are connected parallel-star and the low-speed windings are connected series-star.

For constant horsepower and multispeed, the connection should be series-delta for high speed and parallel-star for low speed.

Because of the variety of possible connections, the starter

for this motor must be designed for the particular type of
motor to be used. One of the most popular manual arrangements requires the use of a drum-type controller to make the
necessary changes in connections. This controller, however,
must be preceded by an across-the-line motor starter which is
interlocked through a set of contacts on the drum controller.

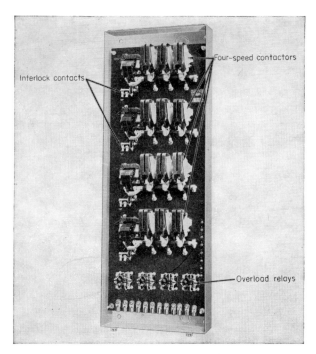

Fig. 3-18   Speed-control starter. (*Cutler-Hammer, Inc.*)

The interlocks must disconnect the motor whenever a speed
change is made by rotating the drum controller. The use of
the across-the-line starter also provides the necessary protection for the motor which is not available on the drum controller.

Magnetic starters for multispeed motors must have a contactor for each speed (Fig. 3-18). The contacts on each contactor must be so arranged that they will make the proper con-

nections to the stator windings for the motor to be used. These starters can be built to give any one of three types of control. The first and simplest of these is *selective* speed control. With selective speed control, the operator may start the motor at any speed desirable and increase the speed merely by selecting any higher speed. To reduce speed, however, he must push the STOP button first and allow the machine to lose speed before the lower speed control is energized. This is done to prevent undue stress and strain on both the motor and the machine.

The second type is *sequence* speed control, which requires that the machine be started in its lowest speed and brought up to the desired speed through a set sequence. The acceleration to the desired speed requires that the operator push the button for each speed in proper sequence until the desired speed is reached. To reduce speed, the motor must be stopped and the sequence started over at the lowest speed.

The third type is *automatic* speed control, in which the operation is like sequence speed control, except that the operator need push the button only for the desired speed. The controller will automatically start in the lowest speed and accelerate through each successive speed to the one selected. To reduce speed, the STOP button must be pushed first. Then the button for the new speed should be pushed, which will recycle the controller to the new speed through each successive lower speed.

The choice of controller depends upon the type of load and the required operating conditions. Keep in mind that the basic difference lies in the fact that selective speed control allows starts in any speed, while the other two require a start at the lowest speed. It is not possible to describe properly the physical buildup of this type of unit in general terms, because of the many possible variations. In any case, however, a magnetic contactor will be required for each speed with the required number of contacts to make the connections for that speed plus the desired protection control. The possible automatic accelerations are discussed in Sec. 2-2, and any of these systems might be used.

3-10   Combination Starters

The National Electrical Code requires a disconnect switch or breaker within sight of each motor. The combination starter includes this switch or breaker in the same enclosure with the starter itself. Combination starters are available in across-the-line or reduced-voltage and single-phase or three-phase types. In fact, almost any type of starter can be had in a combination form. The most common form of combina-

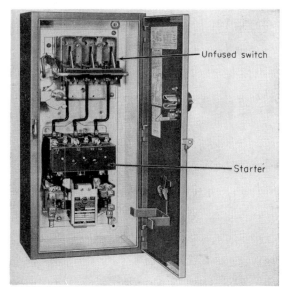

Fig. 3-19   Combination starter. (*Square D Company.*)

tion starter, however, includes a breaker or switch and an across-the-line starter (Fig. 3-19). A combination starter offers several mechanical advantages in that its compact size lends itself very well to a neat mechanical installation. Quite often this arrangement eliminates the need for a junction box or gutter to connect the switch and starter. Electrically, the combination starter offers a protection for the operator or serviceman in that it generally includes a mechanical interlock which requires that the switch or breaker be in the OFF position before the door can be opened. This assures that the circuit is dead whenever the door to the starter is open.

The switch used in this type of unit may be fused or unfused. If the unfused switch is used, then the motor circuit must be protected by another fused switch or breaker to give short-circuit protection. The use of a fused switch or circuit breaker in the combination starter adds short-circuit protection (Sec. 2-8) to the other control functions offered by the starter itself.

3-11 Reversing Starters

The basic requirement of a reversing starter for three-phase motors is that it be capable of connecting the motor to the line in one phase rotation for forward and in the opposite

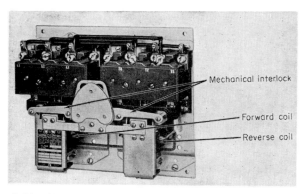

Fig. 3-20   Magnetic reversing starter. (*Square D Company.*)

phase rotation for reverse. A magnetic reversing starter (Fig. 3-20) incorporates two magnetic starters in one enclosure. The line sides of these starters are so connected (Fig. 3-21) that line 1 on starter number 1 is connected to line 3 of starter number 2 and line 3 of starter number 1 is connected to line 1 of starter number 2. Line 2, or center phase, of both starters are connected.

Thus, when starter number 1 is energized, $L1$ and $T1$ are connected and $L3$ and $T3$ are connected. When starter number 2 is energized, however, $L1$ and $T3$ are connected and $L3$

and $T1$ are connected, thus accomplishing a reversal of phase rotation at the motor itself. These units are generally provided with a mechanical interlock consisting of a lever or arm which prevents either starter from closing when the other is energized. Many of these units also incorporate an electrical interlock to achieve the same purpose.

Remote control of a magnetic reversing starter requires only that the push button energize the coil of the starter, which gives a desired rotation of the motor. The STOP button must be wired so as to deenergize whichever coil is in use at the time. The normal wiring of a forward, reverse, and stop push-button sta-

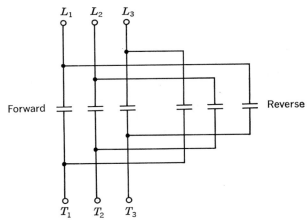

Fig. 3-21   Connections for reversing starter.

tion requires that the STOP button be pushed first when going from one direction to the other. This allows the motor to be disconnected from the line before being reversed and prevents plugging of the motor. Plugging of a motor is the sudden reversal of rotation without first removing it from the line.

If plugging is desirable, then the forward and reverse buttons must be of the double-pole type, with one set of normally open and one set of normally closed contacts activated by one button. The normally closed contacts are so wired that the stop circuit is broken before the start circuit is made, regardless of which button is pushed. Caution should be exercised in employing plugging on any machine because not all machines can stand the severe strain imposed by the sudden reversal of the motor. Plugging can damage machinery. It may damage the motor and at times can endanger the personnel operating the machine. Plugging is used extensively in industry on presses, grinders, and many other pieces of machinery, but these should be so designed that they cannot be damaged by the stresses and strains encountered in this type of operation.

Manual reversal of three-phase motors of the squirrel-cage type is generally accomplished by use of a drum controller or switch between the line starter and the motor. This type of reversal requires that the motor be disconnected from the line before the drum switch is moved from forward to reverse or from reverse to forward. This prevents severe arcing of the drum-switch contacts. Proper wiring of the drum switch requires that it have a set of contacts interlocked with the line starter so that any time the handle of the drum switch is rotated, it will disconnect the motor from the line. This system of wiring also prevents plugging of the motor.

Reversal of single-phase fractional-horsepower motors may also be accomplished by the use of a drum switch or even a toggle switch. The reversal of this type of motor generally requires only that the starting winding be reversed in relation to the running winding. Automatic or magnetic control for reversal of single-phase fractional-horsepower motors may be accomplished by the use of relays or starters. The possible connections for the use of drum switches, toggle switches, or relays for reversing this type of motor are shown in Fig. 3-22.

The reversing starter as such will offer the same control functions as any other starter of the manual or magnetic type plus providing the control function of reversing or reversal of the motor. Should a reversing starter not be available, two across-the-line starters properly connected may be used. When two starters are used in this service, electrical interlock must be used with them to prevent both starters from closing at one time. The electrical connection between the starters should be the same as that used in a reversing starter unit.

Factory-built reversing starters generally are so wired that they require only one set of overload relays. When reversal is required on multispeed squirrel-cage motors or wound-rotor motors, it is generally accomplished by the use of a drum switch between the speed-control line starter and the motor itself.

3-12   Wound-rotor Motor Starters

The starter for a wound-rotor motor consists of a full-voltage across-the-line starter used to energize the field, or primary, winding of the motor and some form of secondary control. The use of the primary starter provides the overload protection

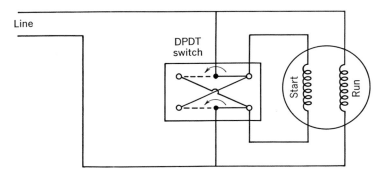

Fig. 3-22   Basic circuit for reversal of small motors.

and undervoltage release necessary for protecting the motor. The primary starter may be either manual or automatic and may be of the reversing type if primary reversal of the motor is desired.   The primary starter should be interlocked with the secondary controller in such a manner that the motor cannot be started unless all of the secondary resistance is in the circuit.

There are several types of secondary control and controllers possible for use on wound-rotor motors.   The most common component used for secondary control is the drum controller (Fig. 3-17).   This unit is merely a set of rotating contacts operated by a handle attached to a shaft along with the movable contacts.   The movable contacts engage a set of stationary contacts which short out resistance in the secondary circuit as needed for speed control.   The drum controller may be of the reversing type or the nonreversing type. It may have several steps for speed control or may only have two or three steps used to give reduced-voltage starting. It is also possible to use a magnetic contactor similar to a speed-control contactor as a secondary controller.

Another type of secondary controller which gives the smoothest speed regulation, over the widest range of speed, for a wound-rotor motor is the liquid rheostat (Fig. 3-23). This type of secondary speed control is generally limited to

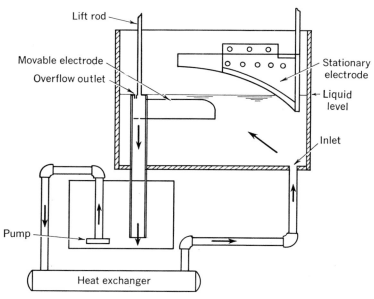

Fig. 3-23   Cross section of a liquid rheostat.

very large equipment such as fans, blowers, and pumps where a constant torque or load is involved. The liquid rheostat consists basically of three tanks of water or other electrolyte. These cells or tanks must be made of insulating material. Inside each tank is a stationary contact or electrode and one movable electrode. The resistance is varied by increasing the distance between electrodes. The maximum resistance occurs when the electrodes are the furthest apart and the minimum resistance when the electrodes mesh. This change in resistance is affected both by the distance between the electrodes and the area of the electrode exposed to the electrolyte. One critical feature of this unit is that the water level must be maintained above the movable electrode even though it moves up and down. This level is maintained by the use of a gate which is fastened so as to move up and down with the electrode. The water or electrolyte must be kept in constant circulation and provided with some means of cooling. Generally a heat exchanger is used for this purpose.

The various types of speed control such as definite time control, sequence control, current-limit control, and frequency control, as discussed under speed-control starters, also apply to wound-rotor motor starters.

3-13 Synchronous Motor Starters

The synchronous motor in its most commonly found form starts as a squirrel-cage motor. During the starting period, the stator is energized by alternating current and may be either placed directly across the line or through a reduced-voltage starter. It is necessary during the starting time to short out the d-c field winding through a field discharge resistor. This resistor protects the field from high induced voltages and also serves to increase the starting torque by serving as a secondary resistance. When the motor reaches synchronizing speed, which is usually between 93 and 98 per cent of its synchronous speed, the starting resistance must be disconnected and the d-c voltage applied to the field winding of the motor. The application of the d-c field excitation will cause the motor to pull into step and synchronize.

The field application relay, or slip-frequency relay, as it is sometimes referred to, is probably the most critical component in a synchronous motor starter. Its function is to apply the d-c field excitation at exactly the proper time. The sensing of the proper time to apply field excitation is accomplished, in the field application relay, by sensing the induced alternating current that flows in the field winding during the starting period. This current is at a maximum when the motor first starts and diminishes in strength and frequency as the motor approaches synchronous speed. At approximately 95 per cent of synchronous speed, the current induced in the field winding has reached a weak enough value to allow the field application relay to pull in and apply excitation to the motor. The use of a field application relay prevents application of excitation current when the motor is out of step more than approximately 75 to 80 degrees. This unit also applies the field discharge

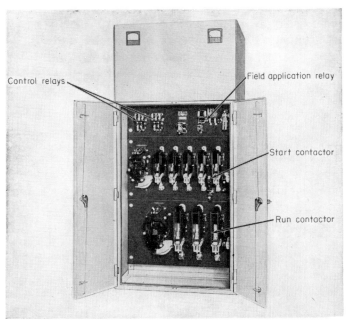

Control relays

Field application relay

Start contactor

Run contactor

Fig. 3-24   Synchronous motor starter. (*Cutler-Hammer, Inc.*)

resistor after removing the excitation whenever an overload or other trouble causes the motor to pull out of synchronism.

The starter for a synchronous motor of standard design consists of a starter, either across-the-line or reduced-voltage type, similar to that required for a squirrel-cage motor, plus the necessary field control equipment (Fig. 3-24).

A semiautomatic starter consists of a manual compensator with overload and undervoltage protection, a field application relay and its contactor, a field rheostat to control excitation, and a field discharge resistor.

An automatic starter consists of an automatic reduced-voltage starter with definite time control, a field application relay and contactor, a field discharge resistor, and overload and undervoltage protection.

There are several factors involved in the starting of synchronous motors where extraheavy loads are to be handled, such as in rubber mills and cement plants. Caution should be used to determine the starting requirements of this type of motor in its particular installation. It is beyond the scope of this book to go into the various possibilities involved in the starting and control of synchronous motors in special applications.

SUMMARY

This chapter on control components is intended to give the student an insight into the many variations in devices used to control the functions of motors. Always remember that a motor can perform only as well as the components in its control circuit. The fact that a particular component is a quality product does not necessarily mean that it will perform well in a particular circuit. The component must be selected to fit the motor to be controlled and the function to be performed.

REVIEW QUESTIONS

1. What is the difference between switches intended for isolation purposes only and those intended for use as disconnecting means for motors?
2. What functions of control can be performed by switches and breakers?
3. What is the basic difference between a contactor and an across-the-line motor starter?
4. What is required to operate a voltage relay?
5. When speaking of current relays, what is meant by pull-in current, drop-out current, and differential?
6. Name two uses for a frequency relay.
7. The time-delay relay has two basic methods of delaying the closing or opening of its contacts. What are these two methods?

8. What are the two basic types of overload relays in general use on across-the-line motor starters?

9. Which of the two basic types of overload relays can have compensation built into it?

10. Basically, what is the difference between a manual motor starter and an automatic motor starter?

11. What is the chief advantage to using an automatic or magnetic motor starter?

12. What is meant by a clapper-type contact arrrangement?

13. What is meant by a solenoid-type contact arrangement?

14. What are the three basic magnetic shapes used on modern motor starters?

15. What is the purpose of a shading coil used on magnetic pole pieces for a-c operation?

16. What is the basic difference between a motor starter and a motor controller?

17. What is a limitation on the use of across-the-line full-voltage starters for starting squirrel-cage motors?

18. What is the common name used for a manual reduced-voltage starter?

19. What are the three basic methods of achieving reduced-voltage starting?

20. What is meant by definite time control?

21. What is meant by current-limit control?

22. Why must the autotransformer type of reduced-voltage starting remove the motor from the line momentarily before applying line voltage?

23. Which gives the higher starting torque, wound-rotor motors with secondary control or squirrel-cage motors with primary reduced-voltage starting?

24. Name several methods of obtaining speed control of motors.

25. What ratio of speed is offered by the consequent-pole motor?

26. What is meant by sequence speed control?

27. What is meant by selective speed control?

28. What is meant by automatic speed control?

29. What is a combination starter?

30. What is the basic requirement of a reversing starter?

31. Is interlocking a requirement on reversing starters?

32. What type of component is generally used for manual reversal of three-phase motors?

4

Pilot Devices

All components used in motor-control circuits may be classed as either primary control devices or pilot control devices. A primary control device is one which connects the load to the line, such as a motor starter or controller, whether it is manual or automatic. Pilot control devices are those which control or modulate the primary control devices. Pilot devices are such things as push buttons, float switches, pressure switches, and thermostats.

4-1 Description of Pilot Devices

An example of primary pilot control would be a magnetic across-the-line starter controlled by a simple toggle switch used to energize and deenergize the coil of the starter. When the switch is closed, the starter will be energized and will start the motor. When the switch is open, then the starter will be deenergized and will stop the motor. The starter, in that it connects the motor or load to the line, would be classed as a primary control device. The switch does not connect the load to the line but is used to energize and deenergize the coil of the starter. Therefore, it would be classed as a pilot control device.

For any given motor, generally there are two primary control devices used. They consist of the disconnecting means or switch and the motor starter. There may be many pilot devices used in parallel and series combinations to control the function of start and stop performed by the primary control device. The overload relays, for instance, which are included in the motor starter, are actually pilot devices used to control the primary device whenever the motor is overloaded.

The requirements of pilot devices vary greatly with their function and their proposed use. For instance, a float switch must open and close its contacts on the rise and fall of a liquid in some form of container. A pressure switch must open and close its contacts when the pressure in some vessel, pipe, or other container varies through the limits built into the pressure switch. Perhaps the best picture that can be drawn to show the difference between primary devices and pilot devices would be the comparison of a contactor and a voltage relay. The contactor is built to carry relatively large currents; therefore, it has heavy contacts capable of interrupting these currents. The relay, designed for pilot duty, has relatively small contacts because the current it is expected to interrupt is very small. In general, pilot devices might better be termed *sensing devices* because they are generally used to sense such things as pressure, temperature, liquid level, or the pressure applied to a push button. The function of these pilot devices is to convert the information that they sense into control of the primary control device with which they are connected.

4-2 Float Switches

Float switches take many forms in their physical or mechanical construction. Basically, however, they consist of one or more sets of contacts either normally open or normally closed, operated by a mechanical linkage. Many float switch units, as well as other pilot devices, employ a mercury switch in place of metallic contacts. The simplest mechanical arrangement for a float switch (Fig. 4-1) would be a pivoted arm having the contacts fastened to one end and a float suspended from the other end. As the water level rises, it would lift the float, thus moving the contact end of the lever downward and either making or breaking the contact, depending on whether the stationary contact were mounted above or below the arm. If a single-pole double-throw action of the contacts were desirable, then one stationary contact could be mounted above and one below the center of the arm. If the float were all the way up, it would make the lower set of contacts, and if the float were all the way down, it would make the upper set of contacts.

Float switches require some means of adjusting the range of operation, that is, the amount of float travel between make and break of the contacts. In the simple float switch, this is usu-

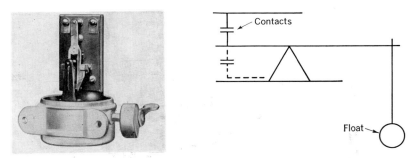

Fig. 4-1   Float switch, pivoted-arm type. (*Cutler-Hammer, Inc.*)

ally accomplished by suspending the float on a rod which passes through a hole in the arm of the switch itself. Then if stops are placed above and below the arm on the float rod, the amount that the float travels before it operates the switch may be adjusted by moving the stops further apart or closer together.

Another system used in float-switch construction to give an even greater range of adjustment is to have the float suspended on a chain or cable which winds up on a reel. The action of the float is then transformed into a rotary motion which actuates a drum-type switch (Fig. 4-2). As may be noted from the accompanying photographs, these are only two of the many possible ways that a float may be made to actuate a set or sets of contacts. Any arrangement that will accomplish this may be properly classed as a float switch and used for pilot duty.

It should be noted here, however, that float switches are also made with heavy contacts and are suitable for primary control of small fractional-horsepower motors. When used for primary control, they are inserted in the line leads ahead of the motor and merely make and break the motor circuit in response to the action of the float.

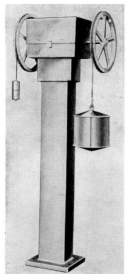

Fig. 4-2   Float switch, drum-switch type. (*Cutler-Hammer, Inc.*)

It is highly desirable when studying pilot devices, if it is at all possible, to obtain several units made by different manufacturers and study the mechanical devices employed in their operation. The student will find that they vary greatly in actual mechanical design but fall into the same basic type of operation as described herein.

4-3   Pressure Switches

Pressure switches, like float switches, are generally considered to be pilot devices. In the heavy-duty models, how-

ever, they are sometimes built for primary control of fractional-horsepower motors. Again, as with all pilot devices,
they vary considerably in their mechanical design. Basically,
they fall into three general classes according to the means of
operation. The first of these is a bellows which is expanded
and contracted in response to increase and decrease in pressure. The contacts are mounted on the end of a lever, which
is acted upon by the bellows (Fig. 4-3). The bellows expands,
moving the lever, and either making or breaking the contacts,

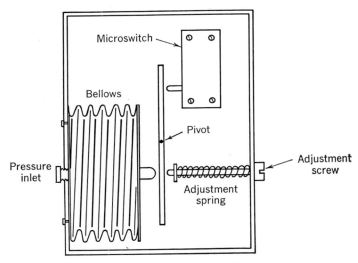

Fig. 4-3   Pressure switch, bellows type.

depending on whether they are normally open or normally
closed.

The second general type uses a diaphragm in place of the
bellows (Fig. 4-4). Otherwise, the action of the switch is
identical whether it contains a bellows or a diaphragm. The
advantage of one type over the other depends greatly upon
the installation and the pressures involved and would have to
be decided in each installation.

It should be noted that pressure switches have a definite
range of pressure where they are designed to operate. For
instance, a pressure switch made to operate from a vacuum up

to possibly several pounds of pressure would not be suitable for use on a line which normally would carry from 100 to 200 pounds of pressure.

A third general type of pressure switch employs a hollow tube in a semicircular shape so designed that an increase in pressure tends to straighten the tube. This action is transformed into a rotary motion by a linkage which trips a mercury switch mounted within the enclosure.

4-4 Limit Switches

Limit switches are designed so that an arm, lever, or roller protruding from the switch is bumped or pushed by some piece

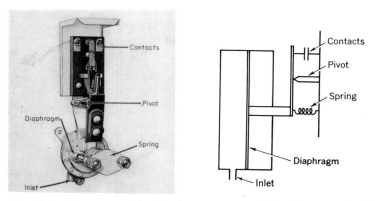

Fig. 4-4   Pressure switch, diaphragm type. (*Cutler-Hammer, Inc.*)

of moving equipment. The movement of this arm is transformed through a linkage to a set of contacts. Movement of the arm causes the contacts to open or close, depending upon whether they are normally open or normally closed (Fig. 4-5).

There is a great variation in the internal design and action of these units, but, again, they fall into two general classifications as to mechanical design. The units intended for rugged use but not for precision control generally have metallic contacts operated directly from the lever action of the switch. Most manufacturers build a more accurate, or precision, unit which employs a microswitch to allow operation on very minute movements of the external lever of the switch. As with float switches, there are limit switches which are built so that a cable or chain is wound up on a reel which forms part of the limit switch. This movement of the chain or cable is transformed to a rotary motion which actuates a drum-type switch. This type of limit switch is used where a great deal of travel must be allowed between actions of the switch.

Fig. 4-5 Limit switch. (*Square D Company.*)

Another type of limit switch (Fig. 4-6) which employs a drum-type switch is designed for direct shaft mounting where the rotation of the machine directly causes a rotation of the switch. The contacts in this type of limit switch must be designed to resemble a cam so that they can close and open with a continuous rotation in the same direction. Many limit switches of this type are coupled through a reduction gear so that many revolutions of the machine are required to produce one revolution of the limit switch, thus extending the range of control offered by the limit switch.

4-5 Flow Switches

The purpose of a flow switch is to sense the flow of liquid, air, or gas through a pipe or duct and to transform this flow into the opening or closing of a set of contacts.   One type of

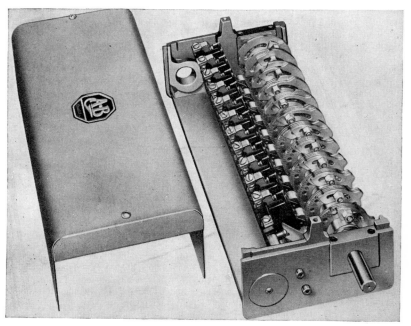

Fig. 4-6   Drum-type limit switch. (*Allen-Bradley Company.*)

flow switch (Fig. 4-7) utilizes a pivoted arm having contacts on one end and a paddle or flag on the other end.   The end with the paddle or flag is inserted into the pipe so that the flow of liquid or gas over this valve causes a lever to move and open or close the contacts.

Another type of flow switch uses a difference in pressure across an orifice flange which is installed in the pipe.   A pipe is run from each side of the orifice to a pressure switch.   The corresponding difference in pressure actuates the pressure

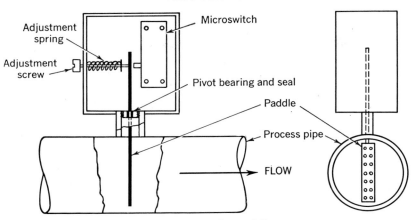

Fig. 4-7   Flow switch, paddle type.

switch in one direction or the other, opening or closing its contacts, depending upon their arrangement.   Such a flow switch
is illustrated in Fig. 4-8.

As with other types of pilot control, there are many other
possible mechanical arrangements for flow switches.   The
student should consult manufacturers' catalogs and study the
diagrams and illustrations in them to acquire a broader knowledge of the design and application of flow switches.

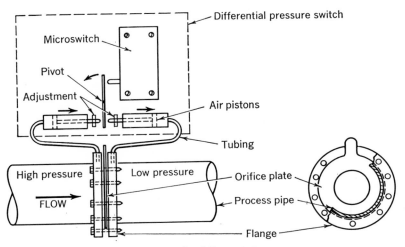

Fig. 4-8   Flow switch, differential pressure type.

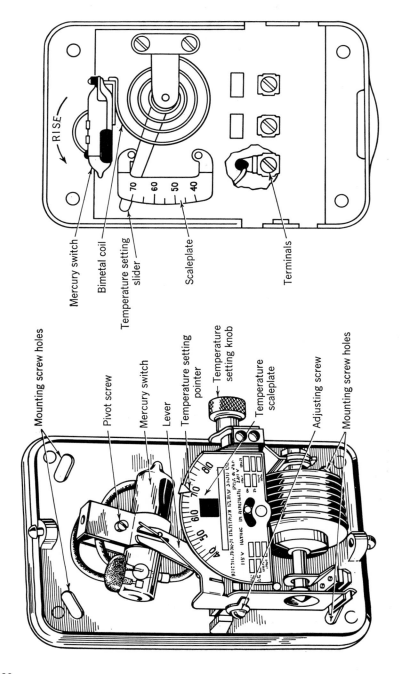

Mercury switch

Bimetal coil

Temperature setting slider

Scaleplate

Terminals

RISE

Mounting screw holes

Pivot screw

Mercury switch

Lever

Temperature setting pointer

Temperature setting knob

Temperature scaleplate

Adjusting screw

Mounting screw holes

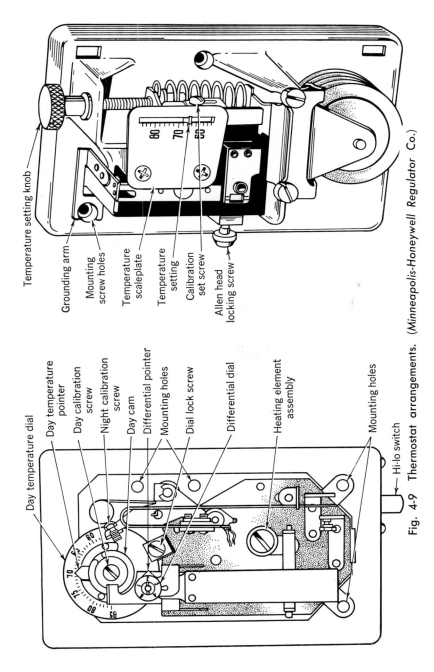

Temperature setting knob

Grounding arm

Mounting
screw holes

Temperature
scaleplate

Temperature
setting

Calibration
set screw

Allen head
locking screw

Day temperature dial

Day temperature
pointer

Day calibration
screw

Night calibration
screw

Day cam

Differential pointer

Mounting holes

Dial lock screw

Differential dial

Heating element
assembly

Mounting holes

Hi-lo switch

80 70

80 75 70 65 80 85

Fig. 4-9 Thermostat arrangements. *(Minneapolis-Honeywell Regulator Co.)*

81

4-6   Thermostats

Probably the thermostat is the pilot device which is built in the greatest variety of mechanical arrangements. Some are made to employ the action of the bellows to move the contacts.

Fig. 4-10   Modulating motor.   (*Minneapolis-Honeywell Regulator* Co.)

Some employ bimetallic strips to sense temperature and actuate the contacts. Many other arrangements are possible with this type of unit. A study of Fig. 4-9 will help the student to visualize a few of the arrangements found in everday use on thermostats. Thermostats for use in motor-control circuits merely open or close a set of contacts in response to temperature changes, regardless of their mechanical construction and action.

The modulating thermostat moves a contact across a resistance in proportion to the change in temperature, thus varying the relative resistance of the circuit. When properly connected to a modulating motor (Fig. 4-10), it can control the position of the motor in direct response to the changes in temperature. The movement of an arm on the motor shaft is directly proportional to the amount of change in temperature. When connected to a damper, the modulating motor can control the amount of air flowing through a duct. When connected to a valve, the motor can control the flow of water or

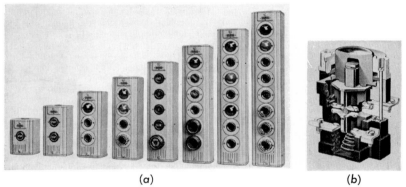

(a)   (b)

Fig. 4-11 (a) Assortment of push-button stations. (b) Cutaway view of a single push button. (*Cutler-Hammer, Inc.*)

other liquids or gases through a pipe. While this type of thermostat is seldom, if ever, used for the direct control of a motor, it can initiate control through contacts mounted on the shaft of the modulating motor.

4-7 Push-button Stations

The push-button station (Fig. 4-11), while probably the simplest of all pilot devices, is the most commonly used in motor-control circuits. Push-button stations are of two general types: the maintained-contact type and the momentary-contact type. When the START button is pushed on the maintained-contact type, the contacts close and remain closed until the STOP button is pushed. This action is accomplished through a mechanical linkage from the button to the set of contacts, which are so arranged that they will remain in either position until moved to the opposite position.

The momentary-contact normally open push button, such as used for START buttons, merely closes its contacts for whatever period of time the button is held down. The normally closed momentary-contact push button opens its contacts for whatever period of time the button is held down. Push buttons also are available in the double-pole style. This push button has one set of contacts that are normally closed and one set that are normally open.

Fig. 4-12   Plugging switch.
(*Cutler-Hammer, Inc.*)

Push-button stations are made up of individual push buttons which may be normally open, normally closed, or double-pole units to give whatever combination of contacts that are needed. The most common push-button station is the start-stop station. Push-button stations are available, however, in most standard labelings to cover the normal control operations and are available with special labels to fit special needs. Also found on push-button stations are pilot lights to indicate when the motor is running, or possibly when it is not running, and selector switches. A selector switch may be used for hand-off-automatic control, or it may be simply an on-off switch.

4-8   Plugging Switches

The plugging switch (Fig. 4-12) is a special control device which is operated by the shaft of the motor or a shaft or pulley turned by some part of the machine. The rotation of the shaft causes a set of contacts to close, and when the power is removed, these contacts cause a momentary reversal of the motor. When the motor is running in reverse, the opposite set of contacts are closed. When the power is removed, this set of contacts momentarily energizes the motor in the forward direction. This sudden momentary reversal of direction of rotation of a motor is known as *plugging*. Plugging is used on many precision machines such as presses, grinders, and other machine-tool operation. The purpose of plugging a motor is to bring it to an abrupt stop, so the plugging switch must not hold the starter closed for any appreciable length of time. Before a plugging switch is installed on a motor, it should be determined that the machine and the motor are built for this rugged operation and that plugging will not endanger the operator.

4-9   Time Clocks

The time clock as used for motor-control circuits consists of an electric clock to drive adjustable cams which open and close contacts at any preset time. There are many versions of the time clock in general use. The simplest clock has a set or sets of contacts which can be adjusted to turn the external circuit on once and off once each day. There are several more elaborate versions between the simple time switch and the elaborate program clock. A program clock may be used to open and close several circuits independently at any desired time. This clock may also be set to skip undesired days so that a program for a period of time, generally consisting of a week, may be set up on the tape, and the clock will make and break the circuit by opening and closing its contacts at each predetermined time.

SUMMARY

The discussion in this chapter is not by any means a complete list of all pilot devices that are manufactured. We have covered the most common and frequently encountered types. Most special pilot devices, such as aquastats, stack switches, relative humidity controllers, airstats, high-pressure cutouts, and suction pressure controls are merely adaptations of the basic types that we have discussed. The control man must above all else be able to look at a strange control device and analyze its function both mechanically and electrically so that he will understand its operation in a control circuit. A thorough understanding of the basic types of control components will enable you to handle most, if not all, new components that you will find on the job.

The best method of becoming familiar with all types of control components is to make a study of the literature which manufacturers are happy to supply free of charge. This literature generally contains photographic illustrations showing the mechanical and electrical operation of the various devices and is usually accompanied by written description of the operation, ranges, and possible uses of these devices.

Quality should never be sacrificed in control components, particularly pilot devices, where the temptation to use cheap competitive units is the greatest. While a thermostat, float switch, or limit switch seems to be an insignificant part of an over-all control system, the failure of one of these pilot devices can shut down the operation of a whole industrial plant. This is especially so if it is located on a critical machine.

Many times a mechanic is overwhelmed by the complexity in size of a control system for such things as central refrigeration plants, central heating plants, automatic manufacturing assembly lines, and other multiple-machine control systems. This fear of complexity is, in fact, groundless if you understand the basic functions of control and the operation of the basic types of control components. The over-all system of complex control is made up of a series of individual control circuits involving these basic functions and basic components which are relatively easy to master. This subject will be pursued further in the chapter on control circuits, where it is hoped the student will be able to see that the most complex control circuits are merely groups of simple control circuits interlocked to give sequence or coordinated control of several machines.

REVIEW QUESTIONS

1. What would be the difference in a float switch designed for primary control and one designed for pilot control?
2. What type of float switch should be used for great ranges of adjustment of float level?
3. Name the three general types of pressure switches in regard to their mechanical operation.
4. What is the advantage of the drum-type limit switch with a reduction gear?

 5. What is the purpose of a float switch?
 6. What is the difference between the ordinary thermostat and a modulating thermostat?
 7. What is meant by momentary-contact push button?
 8. What is the purpose of a plugging switch?
 9. Basically, what is a time clock as used in motor controllers?
10. What is a pilot device?

5

Control-circuit
Diagrams

If you were to find yourself in a foreign land and unable to read or speak the language, you would see the familiar things such as buildings, automobiles, newspapers, and people, but you would not be able to understand what was going on around you.

If you could speak and understand the oral language but could not read the printed words, you still would be dependent upon someone else for a full understanding. The same thing applies to control work. If you have mastered the first four chapters of this book, you can now speak and understand the oral language of controls. Until you master the control diagrams, however, you will be dependent upon someone else for most of your information.

This chapter deals with the written language of control and control circuits. Do not be satisfied until you can read and understand control prints readily and with reasonable speed. When you learned to read English, you first learned the 26 letters of the alphabet that are arranged into combinations to form all the words we use. The same thing is true in the language of control. There are only a few basic symbols that are used to express the meaning and purpose of the control circuit. The chief difficulty is that while there is a standard for symbols,* there is no real standard usage and sometimes it is necessary to do a little guessing as to what a symbol means.

The symbols used in this chapter are those in most common use.

5-1   Symbols

With reference to Fig. 5-1, symbol 1 represents a normally open contact that is automatically operated. It might represent a line contact on a starter, the contact of a limit switch, the contact of a relay, or any other control device that does not require manual operation. Symbol 2 represents a normally closed automatic contact and all that applies to symbol 1 applies to symbol 2 also, except its normal position. The method of telling what operates this type of contact will be discussed under Sec. 5-2.

Symbol 3 represents a manually operated, normally open contact of the push-button type. Symbol 4 represents the same type of contact except that it is normally closed. Symbol 3 for the normally open push button should be drawn so that there is space between the dots and the cross bar, but it is not always drawn with such care. If the cross bar is above the dots, the symbol is for a normally open contact, even though the bar may be touching the dots. Symbol 4 should be drawn so that the cross bar just touches the bottom of the dots, but again it is not always done. If the cross bar is below the dots, then it is normally closed even though the bar does not touch the dots. A good way to remember this is to picture the symbol as being a drawing of a push button, which it is. If you push on the button part, represented by the vertical line, the cross bar will move downward. When it is above the dots or contact points, the pressure will close them. When it is below the dots, it will move them apart and open the circuit.

---

* "American Standard Graphical Symbols for Electrical Diagrams," Y32.2-1954, American Standards Association, Inc.

Symbols 5 and 6 represent manual contacts of the toggle-switch type, 5 being normally open and 6 being normally closed.

Symbol 7 is a toggle switch of the single-pole double-throw (SPDT) type, where one contact is normally open and the other normally closed.

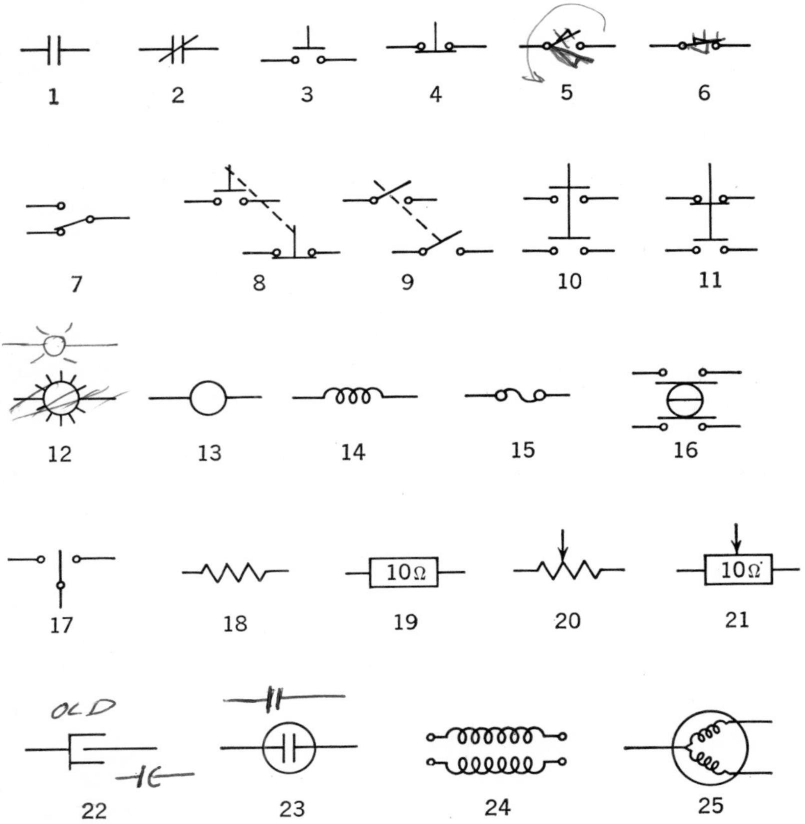

Fig. 5-1 Basic symbols as used in motor-control circuits.

When more than one set of contacts are operated by moving one handle or push button, they are generally connected by dotted lines, as in symbols 8 and 9. The dotted lines represent any form of mechanical linkage that will make the two contacts operate together. One other method that is used frequently to show push buttons that have two sets of contacts is shown in symbols 10 and 11. Symbol 10 has two normally open contacts, and symbol 11 has one normally open and one normally closed contact.

Symbol 12 is a pilot light which is identified chiefly by the short lines radiating out from the center circle.

Symbol 13 represents a coil. It might be a relay coil or a solenoid coil or the closing coil on a starter. Later we shall discuss how to tell which it is. Symbol 14 also is used to represent a coil.

Symbol 15 represents the heating element of an overload relay, also sometimes used to show a fuse. While this may be a little confusing at first, you will soon learn to tell which it represents by where it falls in the circuit. For instance, if it is in series with the line leads, it is a fuse, but if it is in series with the motor leads, it is an overload unit.

Symbol 16 is a rotary selector switch. With a little imagination, you can see that rotation of the shaft would, by cam action, cause the contacts to operate. The same type of switch is shown by symbol 17, but it has an OFF position.

Symbols 18 and 19 show two ways that resistors are drawn. Symbols 20 and 21 are variable resistors. Capacitors, or condensers, are shown in symbols 22 and 23. Symbol 24 is used to represent a transformer. Symbol 25 shows a coil with a double or split winding such as found on some starters when d-c control voltage is used. They are also used on permanent-magnet relays and starters.

With English or any other language, the meaning of a word depends to some degree upon how it is used, and so it is with the language of control symbols. As we progress through the study of control circuits, we shall develop these few basic symbols into words and sentences that will tell the story of what functions are to be performed by the control components represented in the diagram by symbols.

5-2   Diagrams

The control diagram is the written language of control circuits, and it takes several different forms to fit the particular needs for which it is to be used. As with all languages, the same form will not suit all needs. Some things are better expressed by poetry, while others are best written in prose. There are three general types of control diagrams in use.

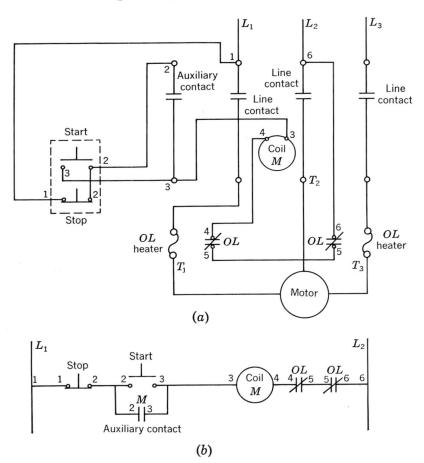

Fig. 5-2   (a) A typical wiring diagram.   (b) A typical schematic diagram.

The first of these is the wiring diagram (Fig. 5-2a), which is best suited for making the initial connections when a control system is first wired or for tracing the actual wiring when trouble shooting.

The second type is a schematic or line diagram (Fig. 5-2b), which is by far the easiest to use in trying to understand the circuit electrically. Most circuit diagrams are first developed by drawing a schematic diagram.

The third type is the one-line diagram (Fig. 5-3), which has very few claims to usefulness except that it is compact and saves confusing lines when many wires must be shown. Its

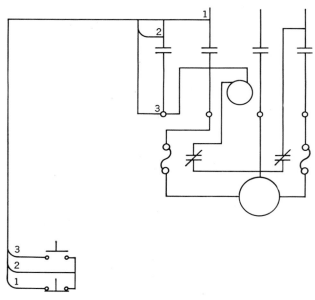

Fig. 5-3   A typical one-line diagram.

chief advantage is for installing already formed wiring harnesses for factory assembly lines.

5-3   Wiring Diagrams

Wiring diagrams (Fig. 5-2a) are developed by drawing the symbol for each component in its proper physical relationship to the other components and then drawing the wires between the proper terminals. In other words, it is a drawing of the equipment and wires more or less as they will be run on the job. Therefore, we can say that the wiring diagram is a representation of the control circuit in its proper physical relationship and sequence. Its chief advantage is that it helps to identify components and wires as they are found on the equipment. Symbols as used in the wiring diagram (Fig. 5-2a) are usually a pictorial representation of the components with the contacts and coils in their proper physical relationship.

5-4   Schematic Diagrams

The schematic diagram (Fig. 5-2b) is a representation of the circuit in its proper electrical sequence. Assume that you have wired a part of a control circuit beginning at line 1 and continuing through each contact, switch, and coil until you reached line 2. If all the contacts, switches, and coils are free of their mountings and the wire is out in the open, you can take each end of the wire and stretch it tight. What you would see would be a straight wire, broken in places by the contacts, switches, and coils. This is what you see in a schematic diagram. Each line from line 1 to line 2 represents a wire and its associated components as it would appear if stretched out in the above manner. A careful study of the diagrams in this chapter will show you that the more complex circuits have several of these wires or lines stretched out and that each of them is a small circuit within itself.

The chief advantage of the schematic diagram lies in the fact that it shows the circuit in its proper electrical sequence. Each component is shown where it falls in the electric circuit without regard to its physical location. There is no diagram that can compare with the schematic diagram for obtaining an understanding of a control circuit or for locating trouble in a control circuit.

To read a schematic diagram, start at the left-hand side of the top line and proceed to the right. If a contact is open, the current will not go through; if it is closed, the current will go through. In order to energize the coil or other device in the circuit, you need every contact and switch closed to form a complete path. In other words, if there is an open contact, the coil will be dead; if not, it will be energized. Remember that contacts and switches are shown in their normal, or de-energized, position.

The symbols used in schematic diagrams must have some means of telling you what operates them and on what component they will be found. Since we have put them in their electrical instead of their physical position in the circuit, the

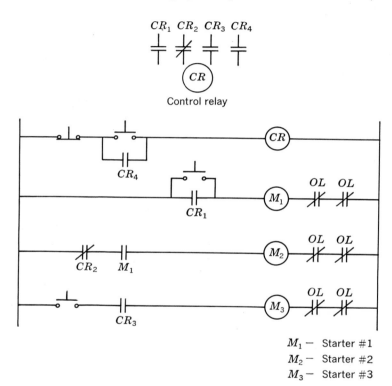

Fig. 5-4   Identification of contacts and coils.

several contacts of a relay might be scattered from one end of the diagram to the other. In order to identify the relay coil and its several contacts, we put a letter or letters in the circle that represents the coil (Fig. 5-4). Each of the contacts that are operated by this coil will have the coil letter or letters written by the symbol for the contact. Sometimes, when there are several contacts operated by one coil, a number is added to the letter to indicate the contact number, generally counted from left to right across the relay.

While there is no standard of usage for the meaning of these letters, most diagrams will have a key or list to show what the letters mean, and generally they are taken from the name of the device. For instance, the letters CR generally are used to indicate the coil of the control relay. The letters FS are used frequently to show a float switch. The letters LS are used to show a limit switch. Quite frequently, when several motor starter coils are shown on one control diagram, such as a circuit for sequence operation of several motors, the starter coil may be shown with the letters $M1$, $M2$, $M3$, etc., for the total number of motors.

5-5 Developing a Schematic Diagram

In order to see the relationship between the schematic and the wiring diagram, suppose we develop a schematic diagram from a wiring diagram (Fig. 5-2). This method of development is highly recommended for use in the field when a schematic is needed but not available. The first step is to number the wires of the control circuit. Start where the control wire leaves $L1$, and number each end of each wire. Change numbers each time you start another wire until you reach $L2$, or the end of the control circuit. In Fig. 5-2a we numbered the wire from $L1$ to the stop button no. 1 and placed the numeral 1 at each end. The wire going from the other side of the stop button to the start button and to terminal no. 2 of the starter auxiliary contact is numbered at each of its three ends with the numeral 2. The wire that connects the other side of the start button to terminal 3 of the starter auxiliary contact and the starter coil is numbered 3. A wire from the starter coil to the first overload contact is numbered 4. The wire between the two overload contacts is numbered 5. The wire from the second overload contact to $L2$ is numbered 6.

To draw the schematic of this circuit, the first step is to draw two vertical lines, one on each side of the paper (Fig. 5-2b). Now draw a short horizontal line to the right from $L1$ and number each end with numeral 1. This represents wire no. 1 of the wiring diagram, which ends at the stop button. Draw the symbol for the stop button at the end of this line. Now draw wire no. 2 from the stop to the start button and down to the auxiliary contact. Note that this is shown as an automatic contact operated by coil M, so it is labeled M to show what operates it. The circuit is continued horizontally across the paper following the numbers on the wiring diagram until you reach $L2$. Be sure to show each contact in its normal, or de-energized, position.

To read the schematic diagram in Fig. 5-2b, start at $L1$, which is a hot line, and follow the circuit across the page. First we come to the stop button. It is normally closed so that the current can flow through, and we can proceed to the start button and auxiliary contact M. Both of these are normally open, so the current cannot go any farther. Contact M closes when coil M is energized, so we cannot complete the circuit that way. The start button can be pushed, which will close its contacts and allow current to flow to the coil M and on through the two normally closed overload contacts, marked OL, to $L2$. This completes the circuit to coil M, and it closes the starter and contact M. When we release the start button, thus opening its contacts, the coil does not drop out, because contact M is now held closed by coil M. The motor is now running and will remain so until the control circuit from $L1$ to $L2$ is broken.

To stop the motor manually, all that is needed is to push the stop button, which interrupts the circuit at this point, causing an interruption of current to coil M and dropping out contacts of the starter. Contact M being operated by coil M is now open, so that when we release the stop button, the coil is not energized again. Note that when the motor draws too much current, one or both overload contacts will be opened, thus interrupting the circuit between coil M and $L2$. The result of opening the circuit at this point is the same as that of pushing the stop button.

While this is a simple circuit and fairly easy to follow on either diagram, the same system for the development of the schematic diagram and analyzing the control circuit will work regardless of the complexity of the circuit.

Suppose now that we add one more start-stop station to the circuit in Fig. 5-2a. The new circuit is shown in Fig. 5-5a.

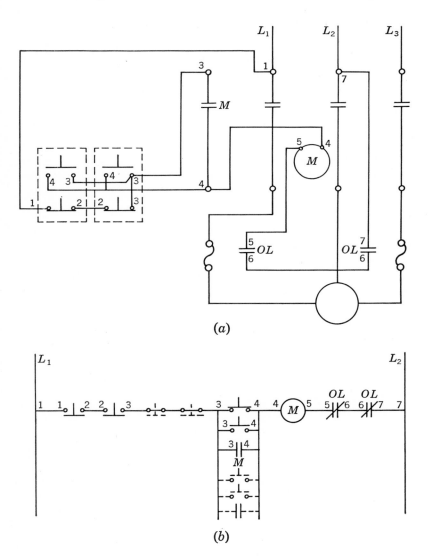

Fig. 5-5 The basic T formation.

If you look at the numbering of the wires in the wiring diagram, you will see that they go from no. 1 through no. 7. This increase in total numbers is caused by the insertion of the extra stop button in the circuit. If we follow the same technique used on Fig. 5-2b, we shall develop the schematic diagram of Fig. 5-5b, which starts at L1 and proceeds horizontally through the first stop button, the second stop button, and the first start button, which is paralleled by the second start button and auxiliary contact. From there it proceeds to the coil of the starter marked M and thence to the first overload contact and the second overload contact to L2.

As in the preceding circuit, the stop buttons will be closed in their normal position so that current can flow from L1 as far as the parallel group of start buttons and the auxiliary contact. Current can flow from L2 through the normally closed overload contacts to the coil M, so that now all that is needed to start the motor is to close one of the start buttons. Since the start buttons are in parallel, either of them will complete the circuit from L1 to coil M, so that it makes no difference which one is pushed in order to energize the coil.

It should be noted that there are two additional stop buttons shown dotted and two additional start buttons and an additional contact shown dotted on this diagram. They indicate additional controls as they would be added to this circuit. Careful note should be taken of this diagram, since it is the basic T formation which is assumed by any circuit with multiple control components used to control a single coil. You will note that all the stop buttons are connected in series from one side of the line or the other. The start components in this case consisting of two or more start buttons and one or more contacts are in parallel. The value of this T formation lies in understanding that if any control component, regardless of its type, is to be used to stop the motor, it will be placed in series with the stop button; if it is to be used to start the motor, it will be placed in parallel with the start button. In short, if you can draw, read, and understand the circuit of Fig. 5-2b, then you can develop more complex circuits by the addition of components to perform the function of stop in series with the original stop button and to perform the function of start in parallel with the original start button.

5-6 Adding Circuit Elements

Suppose that you are instructed to add a limit switch, float switch, or push button to an existing circuit. Then, if this component is to be used to stop the motor, all that is necessary is that you locate the wire connecting $L1$ to the stop button or other components and break it at some point through the new control component.

Suppose instead that you are required to install a control component such as a limit switch, float switch, or push button to perform the function of start for the motor. Then all that is required is that you parallel the new component with the existing start component. These additional components are represented in Fig. 5-5b by those components shown dotted.

It should be noted also that components used to perform the function of stop are normally closed components. That is to say, their contacts are in the closed position whenever the component is deactivated. Those components which are to perform the function of start are normally open components. In other words, their contacts are open in their deactivated state. There is no limit to the number of components that can be added in series with the stop button of the simple circuit shown in Fig. 5-2b to perform the function of stop, nor is there any limit to the number of components that can be added in parallel with the start button to perform the function of start for the coil M.

Consider the circuits shown in Fig. 5-6. The top circuit is the same as that shown in Fig. 5-5b. The current can flow through both of the normally closed stop buttons as far as the start buttons. All that is required to energize the coil is to push the start button, thus closing its contacts and energizing coil $M1$. Coil $M1$, in turn, closes contact $M1$ in parallel with the start buttons, thus maintaining the circuit to coil $M1$.

Now look at the bottom circuit, and you will see that the current can flow from $L1$ through the normally closed contact only as far as the normally open contact $M1$. This contact must be closed in order to energize coil $M2$ through the start button. This contact has an identification $M1$, which indicates that it would be closed whenever coil $M1$ is energized. This means, then, that the motor which is energized by coil $M1$ must be running before we can start the motor which is energized by coil $M2$. If we start motor $M1$ by pushing the start button, coil $M1$ is energized, thus closing both contacts labeled $M1$. The contact in parallel with the start buttons is used to maintain the circuit to coil $M1$. The contact in the lower

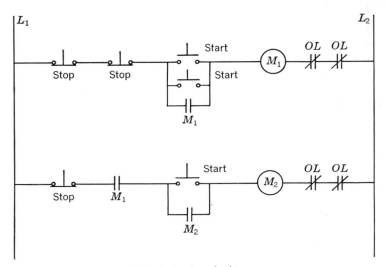

Fig. 5-6   Interlocking.

circuit, labeled $M1$, will be closed and allow current to flow as far as the start button. When this start button is pushed, current can reach coil $M2$. Energizing this coil closes contact $M2$, maintaining the coil circuit and permitting the second motor to run.

Consider what happens if we push the stop button of coil $M1$. This will break the circuit and deenergize coil $M1$, thus dropping out all its contacts. This will open the maintaining contact in parallel with its start buttons and the contact in series with the stop button of coil $M2$. Opening of the contact in series with this stop button will deenergize coil $M2$, which will drop out its contact $M2$, and both motors will be stopped, even though the button we pushed was in the circuit for motor $M1$. Circuits of this type are frequently used for multiple conveyor-belt operation, where the first conveyor must not run unless the following conveyor is running, thus preventing material from piling up where the two conveyors converge.

Actually we have considered only three fairly simple basic control circuits. These circuits, however, represent the majority of conditions that are found in the most complex control circuits. The same type of analysis of the operation of the electric circuit will enable you to understand many circuits which now might puzzle you considerably. In the following chapter on analysis of control circuits, we shall consider many more complicated circuits and develop a system for analyzing their operation.

SUMMARY

In this section we have discussed in some detail the schematic diagram. The emphasis has been put on the schematic diagram because it is the type of diagram which transmits to the reader the most concise and understandable electrical information about the control circuit. The same procedure for reading and understanding the control functions of a circuit applies to the wiring diagram or the one-line diagram as to the schematic diagram. When it is necessary to use a wiring diagram to analyze or understand the control circuit, it is necessary that you trace each wire, beginning at the source of power and noting each component or contact that is in the circuit and what its function might be. It is highly recommended that on the more complicated circuits, if a schematic diagram is not available, you develop such a diagram using the methods put forth in this chapter. Understanding the circuit will be much easier when this procedure is followed.

To read a one-line diagram, the same principles apply except that you must find the proper component by comparing the number of the wire indicated as it leaves a terminal of each piece of equipment. Caution is needed to be sure that you have found all of the places where a particular wire is connected by finding all the points labeled with the same numeral. Again it is suggested that you develop a schematic diagram from the one-line diagram before attempting analysis of the control circuit if it contains more than a very few components.

Should it be desired to have a wiring diagram when only a schematic diagram is available, one can be developed by applying the reverse of the procedure outlined for the development of a schematic diagram from a wiring diagram. Draw each component to be used in the circuit in its proper physical relationship. Now number each wire on the schematic diagram as we have been doing. Then number each terminal of each component on the wiring diagram as it is numbered on the schematic. All that is left is to connect corresponding numbers by wires or lines on the drawing, and you will have a wiring diagram which represents the electric circuit shown on the schematic diagram.

In order to understand the symbols as found on drawings or diagrams made by various people, you should study manufacturers' booklets and control-circuit diagrams that can be obtained from the manufacturers of control equipment. This study will enable you to become familiar with the many types of symbols used to represent a single component just as your understanding of the spoken or written word in English depends upon the size of your vocabulary. The knowledge of words and phrases in English makes it easier for us to understand the spoken and written word as it is presented by various people, and so it is with control circuits. The greater your knowledge of the symbols in use and the components that can be used to perform the functions of control, the better understanding you will have of the various diagrams and circuits as drawn by the many people engaged in this work.

REVIEW QUESTIONS

1. Draw a symbol for a start push button.
2. What method is used to show two contacts which are mechanically connected so that they operate simultaneously?
3. When a push button is intended to be normally closed, is the cross bar drawn above or below the contact dots?
4. What is the chief advantage of a wiring diagram?
5. What is the chief advantage of a schematic diagram?
6. What is the chief advantage of a one-line diagram?

7. Components which are to be used to perform the function of stop are connected in _____ with each other.
8. Components which are to perform the function of start are connected in _____ with each other.
9. How are contacts identified to show what operates them?
10. How is a schematic diagram developed from a wiring diagram?
11. How is a wiring diagram developed from a schematic diagram?

6

Development
of Control Circuits

Control circuits are very seldom drawn or designed as a complete unit. Rather, they are developed one step at a time to provide for each control function that they will be expected to perform. It is very much like writing a letter when the writer has the general subject that he wishes to convey in mind. He proceeds sentence by sentence to put this idea on paper. The same procedure should be followed in developing a control circuit. You must have all of the control functions in mind when you start, so as to provide for each function in its proper relationship to all other functions as the circuit is developed.

6-1 Types of Control Circuits

There are two basic types of control circuits: three-wire circuits and two-wire circuits. These designations stem from the fact that for three-wire circuit control only three wires are required from the ordinary across-the-line motor starter to the control components, and in the two-wire circuit only two wires (Fig. 6-1).

The three-wire control circuit requires that the primary pilot-control components be of the momentary-contact type, such as momentary-contact push buttons. Maintained-contact devices, such as limit switches and float switches, may be used in various parts of the circuit to supplement the primary start and stop control devices. This type of control is characterized by the use of the auxiliary contact on the starter to maintain the coil circuit during the time that the motor is running.

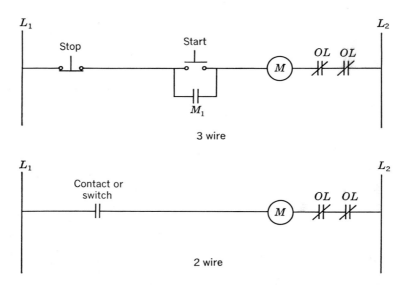

Fig. 6-1   Basic two-wire and three-wire control circuits.

The two-wire control circuit uses a maintained-contact primary pilot-control component, which may be a simple single-pole switch, a maintained-contact push-button station, or any type of control component which will close a set of contacts and maintain them in that position for as long as the motor is to be running. The opening of this contact or contacts stops the motor by dropping out the coil of the starter.

All control circuits, regardless of how complex they may be, are merely variations and extensions of these two basic types. It is the purpose of this chapter to show how each of these basic circuits can be developed into the necessary control of a motor or motors by the addition of contacts or push buttons operated by one or more of the various control components to perform the control functions desired. We shall use the schematic diagram for development of all control circuits because it is the type of diagram which lends itself most readily to the development of control circuits.

The simplest method for the development of a control circuit is to start with the coil and the overloads. Add the primary start and stop control device, which generally, in a three-wire circuit, consists of a stop and start push button used in conjunction with the auxiliary contact of the starter. To this circuit all contacts or push buttons that are to be used to perform the additional control functions are added one at a time until the final circuit has been developed.

Keep in mind, when considering a three-wire control circuit, that all devices intended to perform the function of stop must be normally closed devices and will be located in series with the original stop button. All devices which are to perform the function of start must be normally open control devices and will be connected in parallel with the original start button.

Sometimes a circuit requires that two or more normally open contacts or push buttons must be closed before the function of start can be performed. These contacts or push buttons would be connected in series, and then the series connection paralleled with the original start component. If it is desired that several contacts or push buttons will have to be opened before the function of stop is performed, then these normally closed contacts or push buttons will be wired in parallel and then connected in series with the line to perform the function of stop.

When there is a definite sequence to the action of the various control components, you should add them one at a time to your control circuit in the same order as their operating sequence. Be sure to check the circuit for proper electrical operation after each contact or push button has been added to be sure that you have not interfered with the proper function of any control component which has already been placed in the circuit.

If you have mastered the preceding part of this book, you should have the necessary knowledge of control functions, control components, and circuit diagrams to begin to learn to develop control circuits. Until you can develop a circuit to perform desired functions, it is doubtful that you will be able to interpret or analyze someone else's control circuit as to its proper operation and the functions which it is designed to perform.

6-2   Development of Circuit No. 1

In order that the step-by-step method of circuit development can be made more clear to you, we shall consider our first circuit as a series of jobs done at different times to improve the operation of the original circuit.

The existing control circuit (Fig. 6-2b) is to control a pump which pumps water from a storage tank into a pressure tank. The physical arrangement of the pump and the two tanks, along with the final control components, is illustrated in Fig. 6-2a. As the original circuit stands, it is a manual operation requiring that the start button be pushed whenever the water is too low in the pressure tank. The pump is allowed to run until the tank is observed to be full. The operator then pushes the stop button, securing the pump and stopping the flow of water into the pressure tank.

The owner now desires that a float switch be installed in the pressure tank near the top so that the operator need only push the start button, thus energizing the pump and starting water to flow into the tank. When the level of the water has reached float switch no. 1, its contacts will be opened, thus stopping the pump and the flow of water. The function to be performed by float switch no. 1 is that of stop. Therefore, it must be a normally closed contact and must be connected in series with the original stop buttons, as shown in Fig. 6-2c.

After operating with this control for some time, the owner decides that it will be more convenient if the pump is started automatically as well as stopped automatically. He requests

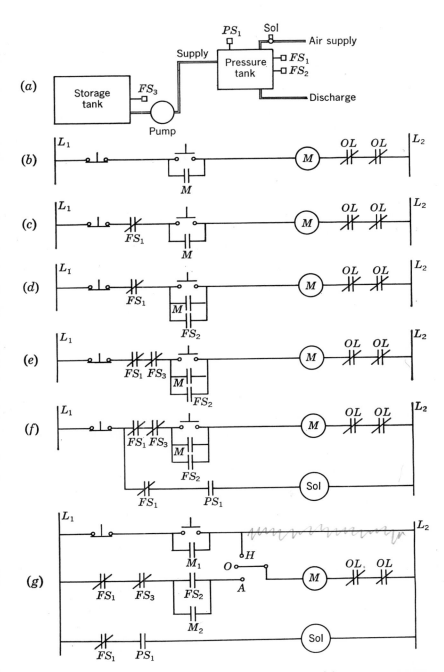

Fig. 6-2 Circuit development no. 1. Automatic control for a water pump.

111

that another float switch be installed to maintain the lower level of the tank. This version of the control circuit requires that the pump be started whenever the water reaches a predetermined low level. The control function desired is that of start, so the float switch must have a set of normally open contacts that will be closed whenever the water drops to the lowest desired level. These contacts must be connected in parallel with the original start button so as to perform the function of start for the motor. This connection is shown in Fig. 6-2d.

After some time of operating with the new control circuit, it is discovered that occasionally the storage tank drops so low in water level that the pump cannot pick up water. The owner requires a control to prevent the pump from starting whenever the storage tank is low in water. Even though this control does not necessarily stop the pump while it is running, it must prevent its starting whenever the water is low. It must also stop the pump if it is running and the water reaches this low level in the storage tank. Thus, the new control performs the function of stop for the pump.

This function of control can be obtained by the installation of a float switch to sense the extreme low level of water in the storage tank. Float switch no. 3 was installed and adjusted to open a set of contacts whenever the water in the storage tank reached the desired low level. Because the control function to be performed is that of stop, float switch no. 3 must have normally closed contacts which will be opened whenever the water level drops to the set level of the float switch. It is wired in series with the other stop components, as shown in Fig. 6-2e.

Later it is decided that the pressure placed on the line by the pressure tank when it is full is insufficient for the needs of the plant. The owner requests the installation of the necessary components and controls to maintain a pressure on the tank by the addition of the proper amount of air to the top of the tank. In order for the proper balance of water level and air pressure to be maintained at all times, air must be let into the tank only when the water level is at its highest position and the pressure is under the desired discharge pressure of the tank.

In order to achieve this, suppose that we install a solenoid valve in the air supply line which will allow air to flow into the tank only when the coil of the solenoid valve is energized. Now we can install a pressure switch in the top of the tank which will sense the pressure in the tank at all times. This pressure switch will perform the function of start for the solenoid valve. When the pressure is lower than the set point of the pressure switch, its contacts must close and complete the circuit through it to the solenoid. If, however, the water is below its top level when the pressure drops, we do not want the solenoid valve to open. Therefore, we require the function of stop in regards to water level, to prevent air being put into the tank when it is not desired.

If float switch no. 1 is of the double-pole variety, having one normally open and one normally closed set of contacts, we can wire it into the circuit as shown in Fig. 6-2f. The circuit for the solenoid valve is a two-wire control circuit requiring that both float switch no. 1 and pressure switch no. 1 be closed in order that air will be placed on the tank by the energizing of the solenoid valve. When either the water level drops and opens float switch no. 1 or the pressure increases and opens pressure switch no. 1, the solenoid valve will close and stop the flow of air into the tank, thus satisfying the requirements of the control circuit as specified by the owner of the plant.

While the circuit of Fig. 6-2f gives a degree of hand operation because the push buttons were left in the circuit, it will be preferable to have either a definite hand operation or a definite automatic operation, as desired by the operator. The necessary changes required to give hand, off, and automatic operation to the circuit are shown in Fig. 6-2g.

If you had been charged with the responsibility of developing the final circuit of Fig. 6-2g, you would have had certain specifications or requirements as to the proper function or operation of the completed circuit. The first of these probably would have been that it have hand, off, and automatic control selection, the second that the pump be controlled so as to maintain the water level in the pressure tank between a high and low point, third, that the pump be prevented from running whenever the water levels in the storage tank were below a given point, and fourth, that the pressure on the pressure tank be maintained by adding air to the tank whenever necessary.   To develop this circuit properly from this set of specifications, the procedure would be the same as that we have followed, assuming that the circuit was built up a little at a time by going back and adding control components to the original manual circuit.

6-3   Development of Circuit No. 2

Our second circuit will be for the control of three conveyors so arranged that conveyor no. 1 dumps material onto conveyor no. 2, which in turn dumps its material onto conveyor no. 3, which is used to load trucks or other vehicles at the shipping dock or a warehouse.

The specifications for the operation of the circuit are:

1. One push button is to start all conveyor motors in sequence from no. 3 to no. 1 or, in other words, from the last to the first.

2. An overload on any conveyor will stop all conveyors.

3. One stop button will stop all conveyors in sequence from no. 1 through no. 3 or, in other words, from first to last.

An additional requirement is that there be a 2-minute delay between the stopping of each conveyor in the sequence in order that the material on the following conveyor might clear each conveyor before it is stopped.

If we are to develop this circuit step by step, then our first step is to meet the requirements of specification 1 that a single push button start all conveyors in sequence starting with conveyor no. 3.   The circuit for this will be found in Fig. 6-3a. Here you will find a control relay which is started and stopped by a three-wire push-button control.   It is maintained during the run operation by a set of contacts on the control relay, identified on the drawing by the letters $CR1$.   Since conveyor no. 3 is required to be the first conveyor to start, the contacts identified on the drawing by $CR2$, which are closed by the con-

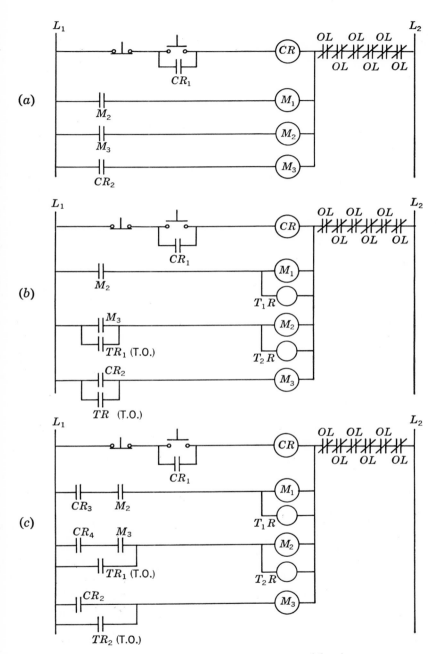

Fig. 6-3   Circuit development no. 2. Sequence control for three conveyors.

trol relay, are connected between the starter coil and the line, giving two-wire control for conveyor no. 3.   This conveyor will start when the control relay is energized and stop when the control relay is deenergized.

In order that conveyor no. 2 be prevented from starting until conveyor no. 3 is running, we can use the auxiliary contacts on starter $M3$ for conveyor no. 3 to energize the coil of conveyor no. 2.   These contacts are identified as $M3$ to indicate that they are closed by energizing coil $M3$.   The use of this contact satisfies the condition that conveyor no. 2 start in sequence, following conveyor no. 3.

By the same token, if we use the auxiliary contact of the starter for conveyor no. 2 to energize the starter of conveyor no. 1, it must follow in sequence behind conveyor no. 2.   The contacts identified on the drawing as $M2$ are connected in series with the coil $M1$ for conveyor no. 1, thus satisfying the condition that conveyor no. 1 start after conveyor no. 2 in its proper sequence.   We have now satisfied the conditions of specification 1 and are concerned with specification 2, which requires that an overload on any one conveyor will stop all conveyors.

The conditions of specification 2 can be obtained by series connection of all overload contacts between the line and each of the starter coils and the coil of the control relay, as indicated in Fig. 6-3a.   If any one or more of these six overload contacts opens, the control circuit to all coils is broken, thus deenergizing the coils and stopping all the conveyor motors at the same time.   We have now fulfilled the requirements of specification no. 2.

While the circuit of Fig. 6-3a satisfies the first and second specification, it does not meet the conditions of specification 3 that the conveyors stop in the reverse order.   The requirement that the conveyors stop in reverse order and that they have a 2-minute time delay between the stopping of each conveyor in sequence indicates the use of timing relays with time opening (T.O.) contacts.   The first inclination is to connect them as indicated in Fig. 6-3b.   A careful study of this circuit, however, should reveal to you that when the stop button is pushed, the control relay will drop out, opening contacts $CR1$ and $CR2$, which will only result in the control relay being deenergized, because contact $M2$ is still closed, maintaining the circuit to coil $M1$, contact $M3$ is still closed, maintaining the circuit to coil $M2$, and contact $TR2$ is closed, maintaining a circuit to coil $M3$. Thus, all conveyor motors continue to run. A modification of this circuit must be made in order that the conveyors may be stopped by the pushing of the stop button.

In order to satisfy condition 3 of the specifications, the circuit, Fig. 6-3b, must be modified as indicated in Fig. 6-3c. In this circuit we have added two contacts, normally open, operated by the control relay and identified on the drawing as $CR3$ and $CR4$. Now when the stop button is pushed, the control relay drops out, opening all its contacts and isolating each conveyor motor starter from the line except for the time-delay relay contacts, which are held closed by time-delay relay no. 1 and time-delay relay no. 2. The opening of contact $CR3$ breaks the circuit to coil $M1$, thus stopping conveyor no. 1. The contact identified as $TR1$ is timed opening (T.O.), so the circuit to coil $M2$ is maintained for a period of 2 minutes, which is the setting of time-delay relay no. 1. At the end of this 2-minute period, the contact $TR1$ will open and drop out coil $M2$, thus stopping the second conveyor in accordance with the specifications. This starts the timing action of time-delay relay no. 2, and after a period of 2 minutes its contact ($TR2$) will open and drop out coil $M3$, thus stopping conveyor no. 3.

We have now satisfied all the specifications for this circuit. The conveyors will start in sequence, beginning with no. 3 and progressing to no. 1 by the pushing of the single start button. Any overload on any conveyor will drop out all starter coils, thus stopping all conveyors. When the stop button is pressed, the conveyors will stop in the reverse order to that in which they started, with a delay of 2 minutes between the stopping of each conveyor.

This circuit performs the functions of start, stop, sequence control, overload protection, and time-delay action. The use of the control relay with its three-wire control circuit provides low-voltage protection not possible with the two-wire control circuit to each of the conveyor starters.

6-4   Development of Circuit No. 3

This circuit will be for forward and reverse control of a motor. The specifications state that it must have three-wire control to give low-voltage protection. It must have electrical interlock, and the stop button must be pushed in order to change direction of rotation of the motor. The first step in the development of this circuit is to provide start and stop in the forward direction. The circuit for this is shown in Fig. 6-4a. You will notice that this is the ordinary three-wire push-button control circuit and satisfies the requirement that the motor start and stop in the forward direction with three-wire control.

The second provision of the circuit is that it start and stop in the reverse direction, which is accomplished by the addition of a start button and auxiliary contact as shown in Fig. 6-4b. The start button is wired behind the stop button so that only one stop button will be required to stop the motor, regardless of the direction in which it is running.

The requirement that electrical interlock be used is satisfied by the addition of the contacts shown in Fig. 6-4c and identified by the letters $R2$ and $F2$, which are auxiliary contacts on the forward and reverse starters. The normally closed contact $R2$ will be opened whenever coil R is energized, thus preventing coil F from being energized at the same time. Contact $F2$ will be open whenever coil F is energized, thus preventing the reverse starter from being energized at the same time. This circuit satisfies fully the specifications that the motor be able to start and stop in either the forward or reverse direction and that the push button must be pressed in order to change from forward to reverse or from reverse to forward. Electrical interlock has been provided so that both starters cannot be energized at the same time.

Suppose now that plugging reversal is required on this machine. The circuit would have to be modified as shown in

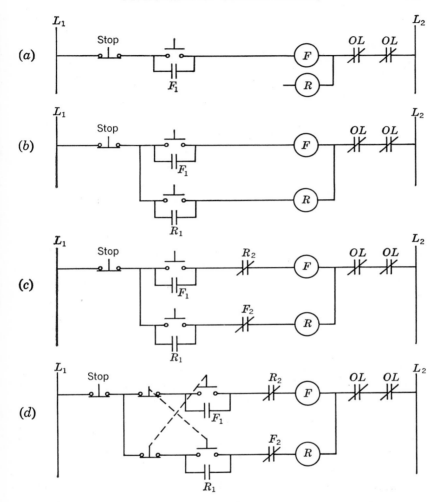

Fig. 6-4 Circuit development no. 3. Forward and reverse control of a motor.

Fig. 6-4d. The start push buttons for forward and reverse would need to be of the double-pole type, having one set of normally open and one set of normally closed contacts. When we push the forward start button, it closes the circuit for the forward starter and at the same time breaks the circuit for the reverse starter.   When the reverse start push button is pushed, it not only will complete the circuit to the reverse starter but also will break the circuit to the forward starter, thus giving plugging action.

This circuit performs the control function of forward-reverse control, start, stop, interlock, overload protection, plugging, and low-voltage protection.

6-5   Development of Circuit No. 4

The specifications for this circuit are as follows.   It must give limit-switch control for forward and reverse running of the motor by the use of momentary-contact limit switches.   It must also provide low-voltage protection.   The initial start and stop for the control system will be by momentary-contact start and stop push buttons.

The requirement that a start and stop push button be used to initiate a control of the circuit by limit switches would indicate the use of a control relay.   The wiring for this is shown in Fig. 6-5a.   Contact $CR1$ is used to maintain the circuit to the control relay during the running operation of the circuit.   Contact $CR2$ is used to make and break the line circuit to the forward and reverse control circuit, thus satisfying the provision that the start and stop buttons initiate and terminate the automatic control of the motor by limit switches.   The use of the control relay and its start and stop buttons also provides low-voltage protection.

The specifications call for the use of momentary-contact limit switches, which would require a three-wire control circuit for forward and reverse.   These limit switches necessarily have two sets of contacts, one normally open and the other normally closed.   When wired as shown in Fig. 6-5a, the normally closed contact of limit switch no. 2 would act as the stop for the forward controller, and the normally open contact of limit switch no. 1 would act as the start contact for the forward controller. The auxiliary contact of the forward starter must be connected in parallel with the normally open contact of limit switch no. 1 in order to maintain the circuit during the running of the motor in the forward direction.

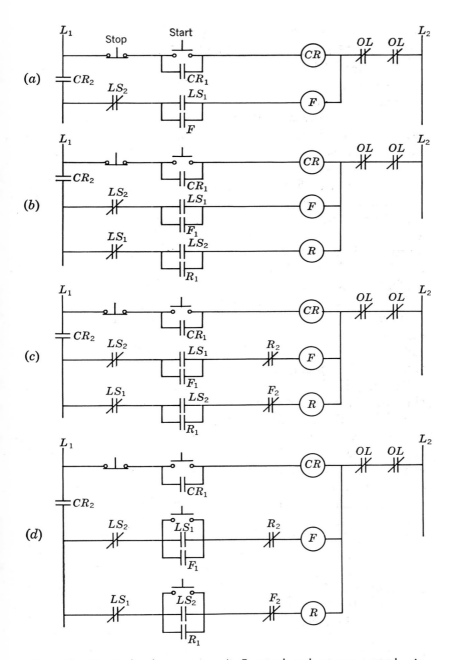

Fig. 6-5 Circuit development no. 4. Forward and reverse control using limit switches.

Figure 6-5*b* shows the additional wiring required for the reverse starter. The normally closed contact of limit switch no. 1 is wired as a stop contact for the reverse starter, and the normally open contact of limit switch no. 2 is wired as a start contact for the reverse starter. The auxiliary contact on the reverse starter is wired in parallel with the normally open contacts of limit switch no. 2 to maintain the circuit while the motor is running in reverse.

This circuit satisfies all the requirements of the specifications with the exception of electrical interlock, which is shown in Fig. 6-5*c*. This electrical interlock is accomplished by the addition of a normally closed contact in series with each starter and operated by the starter for the opposite direction of rotation of the motor.

Plugging is provided in this circuit by the action of the limit switches themselves. When limit switch no. 1 is moved from its normal position, the normally open contact closes energizing coil F and the normally closed contact opens and drops out coil R. The reverse action is performed by limit switch no. 2, thus providing plugging in either direction.

The circuit of Fig. 6-5*c* would work perfectly and satisfy all the conditions of operation if it were always to stop in a position that would leave either normally open limit switch contact closed. This is not very likely to be the case, however, and therefore we must provide some means of starting the motor in either forward or reverse in order that the limit switches can take over automatic control. The circuit additions necessary to accomplish this are shown in Fig. 6-5*d*. Here we have added a push button in parallel with the other start components in the forward and reverse circuits. The function of these push buttons is to start the action of the motor in the desired direction so that it can run until the first limit switch is actuated and then will continue to operate automatically until the stop button is pushed.

Circuits similar to this are used frequently for the control of milling machines and other machine tools which require a repeated forward and reverse action in their operation.

6-6   Development of Circuit No. 5

The requirements of this circuit are to add jogging control in both forward and reverse to the circuit of Fig. 6-4d.   In order to jog a motor, the push button must connect the line to the starter coil while it is held down, causing the motor to run.   It must also prevent the auxiliary contact of the starter from maintaining the circuit when the jog button is released.

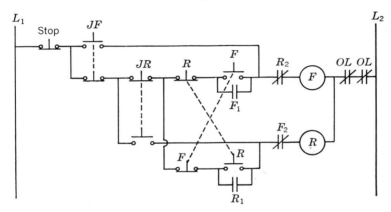

Fig. 6-6   Circuit development no. 5.   Forward and reverse control with jogging.

The circuit of Fig. 6-6 shows two jog buttons identified as JF and JR.   If you follow this circuit, you will see that the jog-forward button has a normally open contact which is connected from the stop button to the coil side of the auxiliary contact for the forward starter.   The normally closed contact of this push button is connected between the stop button and all the other control devices.   When the jog-forward button is pressed, the circuit is made from line 1 through its normally open contacts to the coil of the forward starter through the normally closed electrical interlock.   At the same time, the normally closed contact of this jog button breaks the circuit between the stop button and all the other push buttons and contacts in the circuit, thus preventing the motor starter from sealing in when the jog button is released.

The installation and wiring of the jog-reverse button are identical with those of the jog-forward button, except that it is connected to the reverse starter; its action electrically and mechanically is the same as that for the jog-forward button.

This circuit incorporates many of the functions of control. It has start and stop in both forward and reverse, manual plugging duty, jog service in forward and reverse, electrical interlock, low-voltage protection, and overload protection.

6-7 Development of Circuit No. 6

The assignment here is to add automatic plugging stop to the circuit of Fig. 6-4c. The easiest method of obtaining automatic plugging stop is by the use of a zero-speed plugging

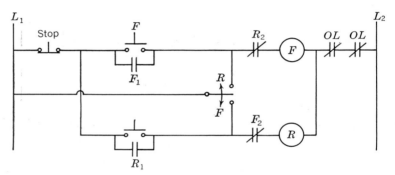

Fig. 6-7 Circuit development no. 6. Forward and reverse control with automatic plugging.

switch. The connection for this switch is shown in Fig. 6-7. The action of this switch is such that when the motor is running in the forward direction, the movable arm of the switch is held in the direction shown by the arrow marked with the letter F. When the stop button is pressed, the circuit is broken to the forward starter, allowing it to drop its contacts and thus closing the interlock contact marked $F2$. At this instant, the circuit is made from line 1 through zero-speed plugging switch through the normally closed interlock contact $F2$ to the coil R on the reverse starter. This will plug the motor in the reverse direction, thus bringing it to an abrupt halt. The stopping of the motor by plugging breaks the circuit of the zero-speed plugging switch and prevents the motor from running in the opposite direction. The action of the zero-speed plugging switch when the motor is running in reverse is such that its arm is in the position marked R. When the stop button is pressed, the circuit functions in exactly the same way that it does when the motor is running in forward, except that now the motor is plugged to a halt by the energizing of the forward starter.

6-8 Development of Circuit No. 7

This circuit is to control a three-speed motor and the requirements are that it provide selective speed control (Sec. 3-9). To satisfy the requirement that the circuit give selective speed control would indicate the use of three simple start circuits, one circuit for each speed, so that the operator can start the motor in any desired speed. To increase speed, he need only to press the button for the desired higher speed. Such a circuit is shown in Fig. 6-8a.

This circuit, however, ignores any form of interlock which will prevent two speeds from being energized at the same time unless such interlock is provided mechanically in the starter. The necessary electrical interlock has been added in Fig. 6-8b. A careful study of this circuit will reveal that it is possible to increase speed by merely pushing the button for the next speed. For instance, if the motor is running in its first speed and it is desired to increase to the second speed, the normally closed interlock contact identified as $M3$ will be closed and the coil $M2$ will be energized. This will break the normally closed contact identified as $M2$, thus dropping out coil $M1$ and deenergizing the contactor for speed 1.

If this circuit is to function properly, then contact $M2$ must be built so that it will break before the line contacts of contactor $M2$ are made. If this is not done, then the starter will energize two speeds at one time, causing damage to the motor and the wiring. The action of the circuit for speed 3 is similar, in that by energizing coil $M3$ the normally closed contact $M3$ is broken before the line contacts for speed 3 are made,

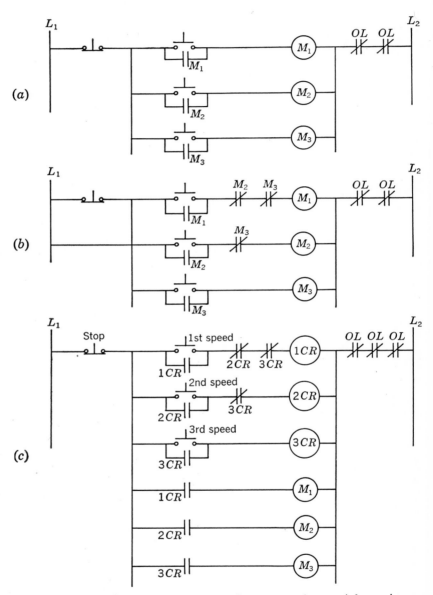

Fig. 6-8 Circuit development no. 7. Selective speed control for a three-speed motor.

thus dropping out either speed 1 or speed 2, whichever is energized at the time.

In order to reduce speed, the stop button must be pressed first. Analyzing the circuit, we see that if we try to go from speed 3 to speed 2, the pressing of the start button for this speed will result in current flowing only as far as contact $M3$. The same is true if we try to reduce from speed 3 to speed 1. If we try to reduce speed from speed 2 to speed 1, current can flow only as far as contact $M2$. The pressing of the stop button drops out any coil that is energized, thus returning all contacts to their normally closed position and allowing the circuit to be energized in any desired speed.

Chiefly because it is difficult to obtain contact arrangements on starters which will provide the make-before-break action necessary in this circuit for interlocking, starters of this type generally employ control relays for each speed, which in turn energize the proper coils. The circuit for use of control relays is shown in Fig. 6-8c. It should be noted that the circuit for the three control relays is identical with the circuit of Fig. 6-8b, with only the addition of a contact on the relay for each contactor coil. Thus, it gives three-wire control to the control relays and essentially a two-wire control to the contactor coils.

While this circuit has been developed for speed control of a single motor, it is equally applicable to sequence control of three motors. If coils $M1$, $M2$, and $M3$ were coils of individual starters for individual motors, they would start in selective sequence. This means that the operator could start any motor he desired and could progress upward in the sequence of motors at will. To go backwards in the sequence, however, he must first stop whatever motor is running and then select the motor desired. This would be selective sequence control of three motors and could be expanded to any number of motors desired.

6-9   Development of Circuit No. 8

This circuit will be a modification of circuit no. 7 to give sequence speed control (Sec. 3-9). The requirements of sequence speed control are that the motor be accelerated by pressing the start button for each successive speed in order until the desired speed is reached. Figure 6-9 is a circuit to accomplish sequence speed control of a three-speed motor using control relays. The contact arrangement on these relays in this type of service is critical, and it must be pointed out that

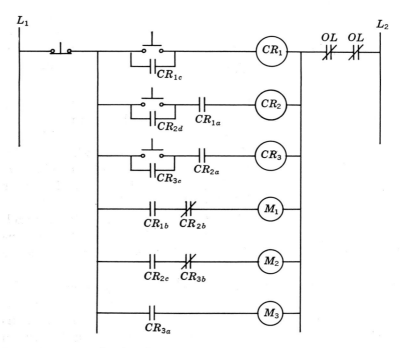

Fig. 6-9   Circuit development no. 8. Sequence speed control using control relays.

normally closed contact $CR2b$ must break before normally open contact $CR2c$ makes. Also, contact $CR3b$ must break before contact $CR3a$ makes.

This circuit will not be developed step by step, because a similar circuit for speed control was developed as circuit no. 7. Rather we shall analyze the operation of this revised circuit. Suppose that the operator wishes to run the machine in its third speed. Then he must first press the button for speed 1, which will energize coil $CR1$.   Energizing this coil causes contacts $CR1a$ and $CR1b$ to close.   The closing of contact $CR1b$ energizes the contactor for speed 1, and the motor starts and accelerates to this speed.   The closing of contact $CR1a$ sets up the start circuit for speed 2, and when this button is pressed, the circuit is complete to coil $CR2$, thus energizing this coil and closing contacts $CR2a$ and $CR2c$.   Also, it opens contact $CR2b$.   The opening of contact $CR2b$ drops out the contactor for speed 1.

Immediately thereafter, contact $CR2c$ closes, energizing the contactor for speed 2 and allowing the motor to accelerate and run at the second speed.   The closing of contact $CR2a$ sets up the start circuit for the third speed.   When the start button for the third speed is pressed, the circuit is complete to coil $CR3$, which in turn first opens contact $CR3b$, which drops out the contactor for speed 2.   Immediately thereafter, contact $CR3a$ closes, thus energizing the contactor for speed 3, which will allow the motor to accelerate and run in speed 3.

It should be noted that the control relays remain energized until the stop button is pressed and that the only way to reduce speed is to press the stop button and then progressively accelerate the motor, starting with speed 1 and increasing speed as desired.   While this circuit is designed for only three speeds, it could be extended to include as many speeds as desired for the motor in question.

This circuit is not presented as the only or most desirable method of providing sequence speed control.   There are many factors involved in a design of a control circuit for a given motor and controller.   The control man will find many variations of circuits to accomplish the same purpose and should try to develop an over-all understanding of the operation of the components and circuits which might be used to accomplish an end.   Attempting to memorize a circuit to perform any particular function is a detriment to the student of control.

SUMMARY

This section of the book has been devoted to presenting a method of developing control circuits. While the few circuits developed here do not in any way approach the limitless number of possible circuits that the student of control will find in actual practice, they should provide the basic principles necessary for the development of any control circuit.

Develop the circuit one function at a time, adding only the components necessary to perform that function. Analyze the circuit after each addition to see that it has not interfered with any previous operation and that it actually does perform the function intended, before proceeding with any further additions to the circuit. If you follow these simple rules, you should have no trouble in developing a circuit to perform any desired function. The greatest danger in developing control circuits is to try to draw a complete circuit at one time. Therefore, it cannot be overstressed that step-by-step development will lead to many fewer hours spent in trying to find out why a circuit didn't work after it was wired.

It is highly recommended that the student practice developing circuits of various types and checking them to see that they actually should operate when wired. If a setup of control components is available to the student, he should at this stage of his study develop circuits of various types and then actually wire them and test them to see that they work. Should the circuit not operate as expected a student should then trouble-shoot this circuit and determine why it did not operate. If such a continuation of the study of the development of circuits is possible, a student will have a great advantage over others who have not had this practice when he tries to apply these principles on the job to actual circuits.

The principles involved in the development of control circuits have been clearly set down in this section of the book, and all that is required to perfect this technique to a satisfactory degree is practice by the student. Your own desires as to your degree of proficiency will dictate how much additional time you spend on practicing the development of control circuits.

REVIEW QUESTIONS

Develop circuits for the following:
1. A motor controlled by a three-wire start-stop station.
2. Add to the above circuit a second push button for starting the motor from a different location.
3. Add to the above circuit a limit switch to stop the motor.
4. A motor controlled by a three-wire push-button station. When

this motor stops, it starts a second motor which runs until stopped by pressing a stop button.

5. Revise the circuit of question 4 so that the second motor runs for only 2 minutes and then stops automatically.

6. Three motors so connected that they are all started by one start button and interlocked so that if any one of them should fail to start, or should drop out, all will stop. The stop button stops all motors.

7. Two pumps started and stopped one at a time by a pressure switch. Provide a manual switch to run the pumps alternately.

8. Add to the circuit of question **7** a second pressure switch to start the idle pump if the pressure continues to drop.

9. Replace the manual switch in the circuit of question 8 with a stepping relay to alternate the pumps automatically each time they start.

10. Replace the stepping relay in the circuit of question 9 with a time clock to alternate the pumps every **24** hours.

11. Four motors started in compelling sequence. Provide a 20-second time delay between the starting of each motor.

12. Four motors started in selective sequence.

13. A three-speed motor with selective sequence starting. Provide control so that the speed may be reduced without pressing the stop button. (HINT: This is similar to plugging without reversal of the motor.)

14. There are four exhaust fan motors in a building. Each fan is also equipped with a thermostat known as a *firestat*. Should any one of the firestats, which have normally closed contacts, open from high heat, it will stop all fans.

P. 127 Par, 3

7

Analysis
of Control Circuits

Now that you have mastered the art of developing control circuits, you should be ready to analyze circuits developed by someone else. The first step in analysis of a circuit is to determine as much as possible about the operation of the machine or other equipment which the motor drives, so that the functions of the circuit can be more readily understood. To analyze any given circuit, it should be converted to a schematic diagram if one is not available. As stated earlier, if the schematic drawing is properly made, the sequence of operation of control should proceed more or less from the upper left of the drawing horizontally across the first line, and then each successive line of the circuit should proceed downward in the drawing. Not all schematics, however, are drawn with this sequence in mind, so do not expect that it will always apply.

7-1 Basic Procedure

The basic procedure for circuit analysis is very simple and should be readily understood if you have mastered the preceding chapter on circuit development. You merely consider the circuit one component at a time and decide what happens if a push button is pushed or a contact closes or opens, realizing that you must have a complete circuit from one line through the coil to the other line in order to energize any relay, contactor, or starter. If the circuit is open at any point, that particular coil will be deenergized and its contacts, wherever they may be found in the circuit, will be in their normal or deenergized position. When the circuit is complete to any particular coil, that contactor, relay, or starter is energized, and its contacts, wherever they may be, are opposite to their normal position. That is, if they are normally closed contacts, they are now open. If they are normally open contacts, they are now closed.

If a time-delay relay is used in the circuit, you must keep in mind whether its contacts are timed opening or timed closing to determine their normal position and their function in the circuit. When relays are used in the circuit, be sure that you consider every contact which is closed or opened by that relay whenever the coil is energized. Failure to consider one contact of a relay may lead to a misunderstanding of the whole circuit. When analyzing a circuit, be sure that you consider every component in its normal and energized positions so that you understand the whole operation of the complete circuit. Do not jump to conclusions when halfway through the analysis.

In the following section we shall analyze several circuits, using a step-by-step procedure which should give you the basic fundamentals of this operation so that you can apply it in actual job situations. The ability to analyze a circuit is a prerequisite to any efficient trouble shooting on motor control circuits.

7-2 Analysis of Circuit No. 1

Looking at Fig. 7-1, it should be obvious that this is a control circuit for a forward and reverse starter. To analyze the operation of this circuit, we shall start with the upper left-hand side at $L1$. The first component is a stop button which is normally closed. Therefore, the current may flow through as far as the normally open start button marked FORWARD. Also, the current may flow downward in the wire to the right of the stop button to a single-pole switch, which is shown in the idle, or OFF, position, and also to the normally open push button marked REVERSE.

If now we press the forward-start button, the current can flow through that button, through the normally closed contact of the reverse push button, and through the normally closed contact identified with the letter $R2$ to the coil F, which is the contactor coil for the forward direction. Thence it will proceed through the normally closed overload contacts identified

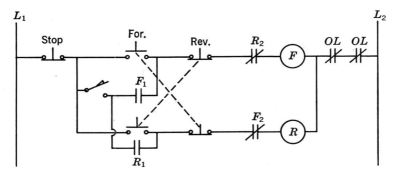

Fig. 7-1 Circuit analysis no. 1. Forward and reverse control for a single motor.

as OL to $L2$. The circuit is therefore complete from line 1 through the forward-starter coil to $L2$, and coil F is now energized. The energizing of this coil will open the normally closed contact $F2$ and close the normally open contact $F1$. The opening of the normally closed contact has no immediate effect on the circuit, because the normally open push button for reverse has the circuit broken ahead of this contact. The closing of the normally open contact accomplished no immediate results, because the switch on the line side of this contact is open and there is no voltage present.

When the forward-start button is released, the circuit from line 1 to coil F is broken at this point and, because there is no maintaining contact around this break in the circuit, the coil will drop out. Suppose now that we close the switch so that it connects line 1 to one side of the normally open contact $F1$ and again press the forward-start button. The action of the circuit is the same as previously discussed except that now when the normally open contact $F1$ is closed, it completes the circuit from line 1 around the normally open push-button contact. When this push button is released, the circuit is maintained through contact $F1$ and the motor will continue to run in the forward direction.

Suppose, now, that we press the reverse push button. It will open its normally closed contact and close its normally open contact. The result of this action will break the circuit to coil F and make the circuit through the normally open contacts of the reverse push button, through the normally closed contact F, through coil R to line 2, thus plugging the motor from forward to reverse. The running of the motor in reverse is maintained through the normally open contact $R1$, which is now closed. The forward starter is prevented from running by the opening of the normally closed contact R. If the switch is thrown to the OFF position and the reverse push button is pressed, we have exactly the same operation as when we pushed the forward push button, except now the reverse starter is momentarily energized.

Now that we have analyzed the operation of the individual components of this circuit, we can sum them up by saying that this circuit provides forward and reverse run. It also provides plugging in either direction and by the position of the switch will also provide jogging in either direction at the will of the operator. The normally closed contacts $R2$ and $F2$ are electrical interlock between the forward and reverse starters. The switch shown in this diagram would be known as a *jog-run switch* because in one position it allows the motors to be jogged in either direction and in the other position permits the motors to run in either direction, as desired.

7-3   Analysis of Circuit No. 2

Looking at Fig. 7-2, we see only one contactor or starter coil which would indicate that this is a circuit for the control of a single motor running in only one direction. Again applying our principle of analysis to the circuit to determine its operation, we shall see that the stop button is normally closed so current can flow through it to either of two normally open push buttons and a normally open contact identified as CR.

Should we press the top push button, it would complete the circuit through the coil identified as CR to line 2. If the designations used in this circuit are standard, it is safe to assume that this is a control relay and apparently has two normally open contacts used in this circuit. These normally open contacts identified with the letters CR will now be closed. The

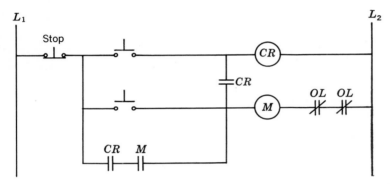

Fig. 7-2 Circuit analysis no. 2. Start, stop, and jog service for a single motor using a jogging relay.

one energized from line 1 to the stop button will allow current to flow only as far as the normally open contact labeled M.

The other control relay contact, which connects the wire following the start button down to the second horizontal line of the diagram, will permit current to flow through this normally open push button, through the now closed relay contacts to coil M, and through the normally closed overload contacts to line 2, thus energizing coil M and the motor. The energizing of coil M causes the normally open contact M to close, which will allow current to flow from line 1 through the normally closed stop button, through the now closed relay contact CR, through the now closed contact M, and through coil M, maintaining the circuit to this coil and keeping the motor running even though we release the normally open start button. The motor can be stopped only by pressing the stop button, which breaks the circuit from $L1$, allowing both the control relay and the starter coil to drop out.

Suppose now that we press the second or lower normally open push button. Current will flow directly from line 1 through the normally closed stop button, through the button we have pressed, to coil M, then through the overloads to line 2, and the motor will be energized. Energizing coil M again closes its normally open contact; but this will not maintain the circuit when the push button is released, because the normally open contact CR is open and has the circuit broken from line 1. When we release this push button, the motor is dropped from the line. Therefore, we can assume that this button is used for jogging of the motor.

This circuit provides jogging with the additional safety protection of a relay which definitely prevents the starter from locking in during jogging service. When the start button is pressed, both the control relay and the starter are energized, and the starter is locked in through the relay contacts. When the jog button is pressed, only the starter is energized, and it is definitely prevented from locking in by the normally open relay contacts.

7-4 Analysis of Circuit No. 3

A careful study of Fig. 7-3 shows us that the top three horizontal lines contain the line contacts of the starter identified by the letter M, the overload heater elements, and the three motor terminals, identified as $T1$, $T2$, and $T3$. The next two horizontal lines contain first the contacts DB and then the primary of a transformer identified as PT. The secondary of this transformer is connected to a full-wave bridge rectifier with the d-c terminals marked with a plus and a minus sign. The output of this rectifier is applied to terminals $T1$ and $T3$ of the motor through contacts DB. The part of the circuit so far considered is part of the internal wiring of the controller, and the remaining section of the circuit contains the external start-and-stop control for the controller.

Considering the balance of this circuit, if we apply our analysis technique, we will find that pressing the start button will energize coil M because all the other components in this circuit are normally closed. The energizing of coil M will

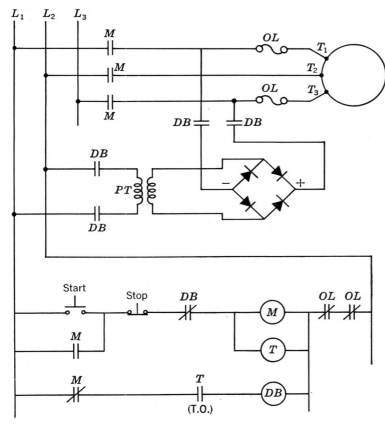

Fig. 7-3   Circuit analysis no. 3.   Dynamic braking for a squirrel-cage motor.   (*Cutler-Hammer, Inc.*)

close all its contacts, and, if we consider this in the drawing, the motor will be energized through the closing of the three line contacts. The auxiliary contact in parallel with the start button will close, thus sealing in the circuit and maintaining the motor in the running position. The opening of the normally closed contact M, located in the bottom line of the drawing, will prevent coil DB from being energized.

Simultaneously with the energizing of coil M, coil T is energized. This seems to be a time-delay relay because its contact T is indicated to be timed opening. If we now press the stop button, coil M is dropped out along with all its contacts, which will return to their normal positions. The opening of the line contacts M breaks the circuit to the motor and stops the flow of current.

The auxiliary contact in parallel with the start button opens, which has no effect on the circuit at this time. The returning of the normally closed contact M to its closed position, however, will energize coil DB because contact T is still closed. We know that this contact is closed because it is designated to be timed opening, and even though its coil is now deenergized, the timer would maintain this contact in a closed position.

With coil DB energized, all contacts indicated by the letters DB will now be in their operating position. The normally closed contact in series with coil M will be open, thus preventing a reenergizing of this coil until the time-delay relay has opened contact T. The closing of the four normally open DB contacts associated with the transformer and rectifier will, in effect, apply d-c voltage to $T1$ and $T3$ and hold this voltage on the motor until the time-delay relay has timed out, thus opening contact T, which returns the circuit to normal at rest condition.

What is the purpose of applying d-c voltage to a motor when you press the stop button? The application of d-c voltage to a rotating squirrel-cage motor has the effect of a smooth but positive braking action and will bring the motor to a rapid but very smooth stop. You may wonder why the time-delay relay is necessary in this circuit. If we did not remove the d-c voltage from the motor at almost zero speed, the low d-c resistance of the motor winding would allow excessive current to flow, thus overheating and possibly damaging the motor windings. This time-delay relay should be adjusted so that it will apply the d-c voltage to the motor windings practically down to zero speed and remove it so that the motor comes to immediate stop.

This circuit seems to provide a normal across-the-line start for a squirrel-cage motor, but in addition provides a rapid, smooth braking effect on its stop. This circuit may well be applied to any piece of equipment where a smooth, fast stop is required or where it is desired to have the motor shaft free for manual rotation when the power is disconnected. It also provides a stop without any tendency to reverse, such as is encountered with a plugging stop. This type of braking is also an advantage where the braking effect must be applied frequently. It requires less maintenance than a mechanical brake, thus reducing maintenance cost. It also provides less shock to the drive system than a mechanical brake and less heating than with a plugging stop. This type of braking is known as *dynamic braking*.

7-5 Analysis of Circuit No. 4

Looking at Fig. 7-4, we see a double set of line contacts identified as $1M$ and $2M$ which connect lines 1, 2, and 3 to the motor terminals. Also in this part of the circuit we have contacts identified as S, which seem to connect some of the motor windings. In the lower control section of the diagram, we have a start button, a stop button, and a coil S, which seems to be some sort of auxiliary contactor. Also, we have coil $1M$, which apparently is a line contactor for the motor. Coil TR appears to be a time-delay relay. Coil $2M$ appears to be a second line contactor for the motor.

In analyzing this circuit, suppose we press the start button, which will energize coil S, since all the contacts and push buttons in this circuit are closed. The energizing of this coil will operate all its contacts, which will energize coil $1M$ and also will prevent the energizing of coil $2M$ by the opening of its normally closed contact. The two normally open contacts S, which connect the three motor terminals, will now be closed, forming a wye connection for the motor coils. The energizing of coil $1M$ closes all its contacts, three of which are line contacts for the motor, thus energizing the motor and starting it

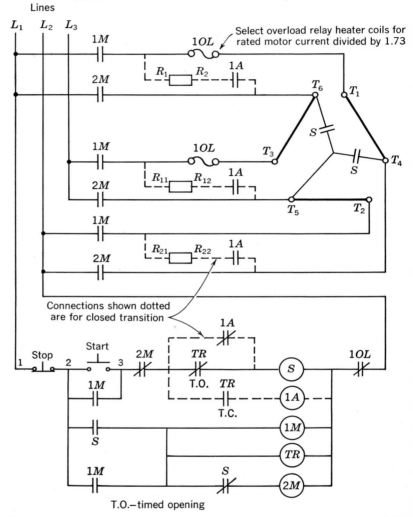

Fig. 7-4   Circuit analysis no. 4.   A wye-delta controller for a squirrel-cage motor.   (Cutler-Hammer, Inc.)

running.   One such contact is in parallel with the start button and acts to maintain the control circuit.   Another contact is in series with coil 2M but at this time it has no effect on the circuit, because the normally closed contact S is now open.

At this point, we have a wye-connected squirrel-cage motor running across the line. At the time coil $1M$ was energized, coil TR was energized and the timing action of its normally closed contact TR was started. When this contact times out and opens, it breaks the circuit to coil S and returns all its contacts to their normal position. An opening of the two contacts connecting the motor windings breaks the wye connection for the motor windings. The opening of the contact in series with coil $1M$ has no effect on the circuit, because this circuit is completed through contact $1M$ in parallel with it. The closing of the normally closed contact in series with coil $2M$ now completes the circuit to this coil and causes its contacts to close, connecting the motor terminals directly to the line, forming a delta connection for the motor.

If you have any trouble visualizing these motor connections, you should draw them separately on a sheet of paper to see that the first connection was a wye and the second a delta connection of the three motor windings. Of course, pressing the stop button deenergizes all the coils and returns the circuit to its normal at rest condition. This circuit shows three resistors and three contacts to connect them, along with a coil and other associated contacts which would be necessary to establish a closed transition for the starting of this motor.

Our analysis of this circuit shows that it is a wye-delta-type motor controller used for the purpose of giving a reduced-voltage effect to the starting of this motor as discussed in a previous chapter. In applications where a closed transition is necessary or desirable, the additional connections are shown for adding resistance to bridge the motor connections during the transfer from wye to delta. This is a rather common circuit and deserves some concentrated study as to principle of operation. Again, however, a warning is in order not to memorize this circuit as being the only possible way to give wye-delta starting to squirrel-cage motors. The use of the time-delay relay with its timed opening contacts gives us a definite time type of acceleration for this control circuit. This controller, as you may have noticed, involves a two-pole and two three-pole magnetic contactors along with the necessary mechanical interlock to assure a sequence of operation and to prevent two connections at the same time, which would cause a short circuit.

7-6   Analysis of Circuit No. 5

Considering the circuit of Fig. 7-5, the resistance in series with the motor leads would seem to indicate that this is a pri-

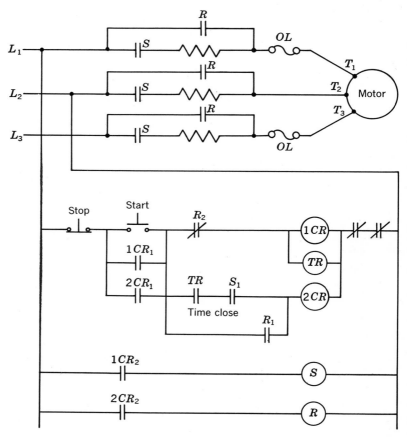

Fig. 7-5   Circuit analysis no. 5.   Primary-resistance reduced-voltage starter.

mary-resistance reduced-voltage starter.   Looking at the control section of the diagram, we have what seems to be an ordinary three-wire control circuit to energize coils $1CR$ and TR.

If we press the start button, current may flow through the normally closed stop, and start-button contact $R2$ and coils $1CR$ and TR will be energized. The energizing of coil $1CR$ will cause all its contacts to close. Contact $1CR1$ is in parallel with the start button and will perform the function of maintaining the circuit to the coil. Contact $1CR2$ will close and energize coil S. The energizing of this coil will cause the line contacts S to close and will energize the motor through the series resistances. The presence of resistance in series with the motor leads will cause a reduced voltage to be applied to the motor, thus reducing the inrush current to the motor and providing reduced-voltage starting.

The motor is now accelerating under reduced voltage, and the time-delay relay TR is timing out. When relay TR times out, it will close contact TR. When this contact closes, it will energize coil $2CR$ because contact $S1$ is closed by coil S. The energizing of coil $2CR$ will cause contact $2CR1$ to close. This contact is in parallel with the start button and forms an additional maintaining circuit for the coil. The closing of contact $2CR2$ causes coil R to be energized, closing the line contacts identified as R. These contacts are in parallel with the resistors and effectively short them out of the circuit, thus applying full line voltage to the motor, which will enable it to accelerate to its full speed and run across the line.

The energizing of coil R also closes contact $R1$, which is in parallel with contacts TR and $S1$. The opening of contact $R2$ will cause the dropping out of coils $1CR$ and TR. The contacts associated with these two coils will now return to their normal position, and we shall have the motors running through the control circuit, which consists of the stop-button contact $2CR1$, contact $R1$, and coil $2CR$. This circuit maintains the circuit to the run coil through contact $2CR2$. Should the stop button now be pressed, all contacts would return to their normal position and all coils would be deenergized, thus opening the line contacts to the motor, and the motor would come to a stop.

This circuit obviously is one for a primary-resistance reduced-voltage starter. Again it must be pointed out that this is only one of the many arrangements of coils and contacts which could be used to achieve the same results. Different manufacturers will use variations of a similar circuit in the control of their starters, but the basic principle of operation is the same if a definite time sequence of starting is employed.

This circuit could be expanded to give several more stages of acceleration by the addition of more units of resistance in series with the motor with a control relay and a time-delay relay for each step or stage of acceleration. This is a two-stage, or two-step, starter, since it provides two steps of acceleration, one under reduced voltage and one under full voltage.

The only critical adjustment in this circuit will be found in the time-delay relay TR, which must not be allowed to maintain the motor under reduced voltage longer than the time it takes to accelerate to its maximum speed under reduced-voltage conditions. Prolonged operation of the motor under reduced voltage may quite possibly overheat and damage the motor windings and cause the resistance elements to be seriously damaged or burn out.

This controller consists of a start contactor S, which must be three-pole, and a run contactor R, which also must be three-pole. In addition to the two contactors, there are two control relays and one time-delay relay. This equipment would be found generally mounted in one enclosure with the start-stop push-button station either mounted on the door of this enclosure or separately wired to any convenient location in the building.

At this stage in your study of controls and analysis of control circuits, you should consider a circuit from the standpoint of what would happen if a particular coil burned out or a particular contact failed to open or close, as the case may be. For instance, suppose that the time-delay relay TR were to have a burnt-out coil. What would be the effect on this circuit? The circuit would function up through the closing of the start contactor S, and the motor would be energized under reduced-voltage conditions. If contact TR does not close, however, then the second control relay cannot be energized and the run contactor cannot be energized. Thus, the motor would continue to run under reduced-voltage conditions. The current under this condition is such that it will open the overload relay contacts and will drop out coil $1CR$, thus stopping the motor and returning it to its normal position. These overload units should be manual reset units so that the operator will have to reset them and determine the cause of trouble before restarting the motor. This will give overload protection and incomplete sequence protection (Sec. 2-15).

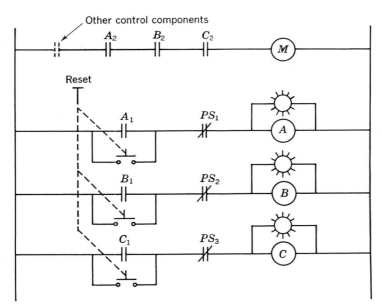

Fig. 7-6   Circuit analysis no. 6.   Lockout circuit.

7-7   Analysis of Circuit No. 6

The circuit of Fig. 7-6 is a partial circuit used to illustrate a lockout circuit, which is extensively used where malfunction of some part of the equipment must require attention by the operator before the equipment is restarted. Looking at the circuit of Fig. 7-6, you will see dotted a contact which represents the normal control components such as start and stop buttons, limit switches, or other devices which normally start and stop the machine. This circuit concerns itself only with the lockout components. The normally closed contacts represented as $PS1, 2, 3$ are pressure switches which will open only when the required pressure is not maintained in their particular part of the machine or process. Coils A, B, C are relay coils paralleled by pilot lights.

To start the operation of this equipment, it is necessary to press the reset button, which will close the three associated and mechanically interlocked switches. The three relays will be energized, thus closing their normally open contacts. Contacts $A1, B1, C1$ are used to maintain the coil circuit. Contacts $A2, B2, C2$ are maintained in their closed position as long as the operation of the pressure switches is normal, thus enabling the normal control components to energize coil M at will. If the pressure drops or rises, as the case may be, from its normal value at any one of the three places where pressure switches are located, it will open one of the normally closed contacts. For instance, if $PS1$ opens, coil A will be deenergized, which will open contact $A2$ and drop out the motor. At the same time, contact $A1$ will open. If the proper pressure returns to pressure switch no. 1, its contact will close but coil A will not be reenergized, because the circuit is broken at contact $A1$. The pilot light in parallel with this coil will be out and will indicate which of the protective circuits is not functioning. The operator will know that pressure switch no. 1 was the cause of the shutdown of the equipment. In order to restore the machine to operation, the pressure sensed by pressure switch no. 1 must be restored to normal. Then the reset button must be pressed in order to energize coil A, thus closing its contacts and allowing the normal operation of the control circuit. Of course, the same procedure will apply to the second and third pressure switches and associated contacts and coils.

This type of circuit is generally applied to fully automatic equipment, where the machine or process is allowed to start and stop by itself under the control of pilot devices which sense the condition of the process or material as the machine does its work. When machinery operates under these conditions, it is generally desirable to have some means to stop the process whenever a malfunction occurs and to prevent it from restarting until it has received the attention of an operator.

SUMMARY

The preceding circuits and their analysis should form a basis upon which you can build a skill of analyzing circuits as found in everyday use in industry and on the job. While these circuits do not in any way represent all or even a major part of the possibilities in motor control, the procedure and method of analyzing their operation, if properly understood, may be applied to any and all control circuits and followed through to a complete understanding of the operation of the equipment and control components associated with it.

The student who wishes to obtain proficiency in control will apply these basic principles to other circuits which are at his disposal until he is satisfied that he can, with reasonable speed, interpret and analyze control circuits of all types.

The danger in circuit analysis lies in the tendency to jump to conclusions, that is, to decide what the circuit does and how it operates when you have analyzed only a fraction of all of its possibilities. Learn to study a circuit contact by contact and coil by coil until you have completely traced its operation through its normal sequence from beginning to end, and you will save many headaches in the future.

There are no review questions at the conclusion of this section. The procedure you should follow is to obtain additional circuits and practice analyzing them until you obtain proficiency. The mark of distinction between a good trouble shooter and a poor trouble shooter generally lies in the ability to analyze the control circuit and determine quickly which of the many components could cause the malfunction of the machine which he is trying to correct.

8

Maintaining
Control Equipment

If there is a single rule which applies to all maintenance procedure in all plants and under all conditions, it is *be careful*. Carelessness and failure to observe safety precautions are two things that the maintenance man cannot afford.

8-1 General Procedure

The first procedure in any organized maintenance of equipment should be periodic inspection to prevent serious trouble from arising. This inspection should include not only electrical equipment but the machine as well, should point up the wear and tear on the electrical equipment, and should provide a basis on which replacement of parts and correction of danger spots can be taken care of before they cause serious trouble.

One of the greatest causes of failure of control systems is dust, grease, oil, and dirt, which must be removed periodically in order that the equipment may function properly. The removal of dust and dirt may be accomplished by dusting or wiping with rags, but this is not always effective with oil and grease. These substances generally should be removed by the use of a solvent such as carbon tetrachloride. Care should be exercised whenever these solvents are used because the inhaling of any appreciable quantity of their fumes is quite likely to be very harmful. Therefore, adequate ventilation should always be provided.

Periodic inspection should always include a check for overheating of electrical equipment and mechanical parts, because excess heat is always an indication of trouble to come. The value of checking for excess heat depends upon your knowledge of the proper operating temperature of bearings, coils, contacts, transformers, and the many other pieces of equipment associated with machinery, motors, and control.

Bearings of motors and mechanical equipment should be checked for proper lubrication. It is very seldom, however, that bearings of electrical equipment such as starters and switches are oiled. They are designed to operate dry, and, generally speaking, oiling the bearings will eventually cause a gum to form, causing the equipment to malfunction.

One of the other most frequent causes of failure of control equipment is loose bolts and electrical connections. Each connection should be periodically checked for tightness, and the inspection should include the checking of possible loose bolts and nuts on the equipment.

Short circuits and grounds in the electrical wiring may be prevented by proper inspection of insulation and by using a Megger insulation tester on motors and cables in associated equipment.

If you are to maintain the same equipment over a period of time, the first law to follow is to be familiar with your equipment. Know your equipment mechanically and electrically so that you will sense trouble before it develops.

The second law is to be observant. Whenever you pass a piece of equipment for which you are responsible, listen and look. Quite often this is all that is necessary to tell you that trouble is on its way. Good maintenance procedure can be summed up in a very few words: Keep it tight, keep it clean, keep it lubricated, and inspect it frequently.

8-2   Maintenance of Motor Starters

The most frequent trouble encountered with motor starters is contact trouble.   Contacts should be inspected for excessive burning or pitting and for proper alignment.   If they are pitted, they may be filed or sandpapered, but care must be exercised not to remove too much contact surface or to change their shape appreciably.   If the contacts are made of copper and are subject to heat and oxygen, as they are on closing and opening of the circuit, copper oxide may be formed on the surface of the contact.   This oxide is an insulator which must be removed if it covers a large part of the contact surface.   Most contacts made of copper are arranged to be of the wiping type, which allows the mechanical closing of the contacts to remove this oxide as it forms.   If the contacts are silverplated, the silver oxide is a good conductor and need not be removed; in fact, silver contacts should never be filed unless very seriously pitted.

The contacts should be inspected not only for pitting but for proper alignment and for proper contact pressure.   Improper alignment or lack of contact pressure will cause excessive arcing and pitting of the contacts.

8-3   Causes of Trouble

One of the most frequent causes of failure of automatic equipment is improper adjustment of contacts and time-delay circuits.   Generally, the manufacturer of controllers for automatic equipment will supply the proper contact clearance distances and other information necessary for the proper timing of the circuit.   This information should be readily available to the maintenance man so that he can periodically correct these adjustments.   A check of these adjustments should be part of the regular inspection of this type of equipment.

The second most prevalent cause of trouble in motor starters and contactors is coil burnout.   Coils on modern-day starters are well built and well insulated, which has eliminated considerable trouble due to vibration and moisture.   Coils are still subject to burnout, however, chiefly because of one of two things. The most frequent cause of coil burnout is failure of the contactor magnet circuit to close, causing a gap in this circuit which increases the normal current through the coil to dangerous levels. The normal current to start the movement of a magnetic pole piece may be as high as 40 or 45 amperes, but as the magnet circuit is closed, this current usually drops to a very low value of 1 to $1\frac{1}{2}$ amperes, which is all that is required to maintain the magnetic circuit. If this circuit does not close, the coil will maintain a current somewhere in between these two values, which can very easily cause it to overheat and burn its windings.

The second most frequent cause of coil burnout is improper voltage. If the voltage applied to the coil is exceedingly high, the current through the coil can reach dangerous levels and cause it to burn out. If the voltage applied to the coil drops so low that the magnetic circuit cannot be completed we have a gap which will cause exceedingly high currents and cause coil burnout. In view of the above-mentioned causes, the proper procedure when it is found that a coil has burned out on a starter is to check the mechanical linkage to see that the contactor can close completely and to check the voltage applied to the coil under load to see that it is sufficient but not excessive. Check for spring tension to see that the springs themselves are not causing the magnetic circuit to remain partially open.

Should the contactor be equipped with flexible leads, they should be checked for fraying and broken strands and should be replaced if these conditions exist. Should the starter be equipped with arc shields, they should be inspected for proper alignment around the contacts. They should be checked for accumulations of dust and dirt, and if carbon deposits have built up on the inside of these shields, they should be carefully removed, since carbon reduces the arc path and can be the cause of serious arc-overs, particularly under high-voltage conditions.

Spring tension for proper contact pressure is very important in a starter and should be checked against manufacturer's standards if they are available. They should at least be checked to see that each contact has approximately the same spring tension so that the contact pressure will be equal on each contact. Improper or unequal spring tension is one of the most common causes of contact chatter and starter hum, so be sure that when these conditions exist, you check the spring tension on every contact to determine if it is sufficient and that they are all equal.

8-4   Maintenance of Relays

Generally speaking, the maintenance of voltage relays is the same as that for motor starters and contactors with only the additional precaution that, in general, relays operate on lower currents and thus are provided with less power. This lower power demands a smoother, easier operating mechanical linkage and mechanism and thus requires more careful attention to the matters concerning it.

Current relays must be checked to see that they are receiving the proper amount of current for closing their contacts and that the spring tension and contact spacing are correct to give the proper pull-in and drop-out currents. Wear of contact surface and change in spring tension can cause a great deal of variance in these values of pull-in, drop-out, and differential currents, which may make the circuit operate in a manner detrimental to the equipment.

Overload relays are devices which normally do not operate for long periods of time; therefore, they are subject to accumulations of corrosion, dust, and dirt, which must be removed after periodic checking to see that they can operate when needed. If proper equipment is available, overload relays should be tripped by current periodically to see that they do function. Excessive tripping of overload relays is generally not an indication of relay failure so much as it is of overload on the circuit. The maintenance man should first determine the current value at which the overload unit actually trips and compare this with the allowable current to determine whether the fault lies with the overload unit or with the circuit itself.

Time-delay relays, whether of the pneumatic type or the dashpot type, require periodic adjustment to compensate for normal changes in their operating characteristics. The dashpot relay should be checked for dust and other foreign matter in the oil reservoir, since any impurities in the oil will affect the accuracy of the timing of the dashpot.

Quite frequently, relay contacts may be of the make-before-break or break-before-make type, and here again spring tension and contact spacing become very important and require a check to determine that they are functioning as they were intended to.

8-5   Maintenance of Pilot Devices

Generally speaking, pilot devices require very little maintenance other than a check of their mechanical operation and their contact condition. Where the pilot device is a form of pressure switch or vacuum switch, the range of its operation should be checked occasionally to see that the contacts open and close at the pressure they were set up to operate on. The contact surfaces should be examined to see that they have not accumulated a coating of copper oxide, dust, or oil. They should be operated through their pressure range several times to check for consistency of operation.

Float switches are subject to troubles because of float rods being bent or because of water in the float due to a leak. A check of the proper operation of the float, the float rod, and the mechanical linkage to the float switch itself will determine the amount of wear and can generally indicate a replacement of parts before any serious trouble can develop. Of course, contact condition is a must on checking this as well as other pilot devices.

When limit switches are an integral part of a control system, they are a very likely source of trouble because they perform many thousands of operations per day on an active piece of equipment. They are prone to mechanical failure because of worn bearings and cam surfaces as well as contact surfaces and spring tension. The only solution to limit switch failure is frequent and accurate inspection to determine their mechanical and electrical condition. When the mechanical condition of a limit switch becomes questionable, it should be replaced or repaired before it causes serious trouble with the other equipment.

8-6   Maintenance of Brakes and Clutches

The chief cause of failure of brakes is, of course, worn brake lining or brake disks, as the case may be. This is an inexcusable cause of failure, however, if periodic inspection is employed. Never allow brake lining to reach the dangerous condition of wear.

The second most prevalent cause of brake failure is excessive wear and improper adjustment of the linkage from the electric solenoid or other operating device to the brake shoe or brake disk. These must be maintained in their proper mechanical alignment and condition. Improper linkage adjustment is a frequent cause of coil burnout on brake solenoids, since it does not provide the proper seal to the magnetic circuit, which in turn causes excessive current to flow in the solenoid coil.

Solenoid-operated clutches are subject to the same types of trouble as solenoid-operated brakes. Therefore, the inspection and maintenance procedure for these units should be the same as that for brakes.

SUMMARY

While this chapter has attempted to point up some of the basic principles of good maintenance, the actual maintenance of a specific piece of equipment must be determined by its operating cycle, the complexity of its equipment, and the amount of maintenance time available. The chief difficulty in most maintenance situations is a lack of the understanding of the word "maintenance," which means to *maintain* the equipment in operation as compared with repairing the equipment after it has broken down. Again, inspect it, keep it clean, and keep it tight, and you will be doing maintenance, not repair.

REVIEW QUESTIONS

1. What is the chief cause of coil burnout on starters, contactors, and relays?

2. Can copper oxide be the cause of trouble on contacts?

3. Should silver contacts be filed frequently?

4. What are some of the results of improper spring tension on starters?

5. What is a probable cause of contact chatter and starter hum on motor starters?

6. What would you expect to be the result of low voltage applied to the coil of a magnetic starter?

7. What is the proper procedure to determine the cause of too frequent tripping of overload relays?

8. What is a likely result of having a float half full of water when it operates a float switch?

9. What is likely to happen if an accumulation of carbon is allowed to form in the arc shields of a starter or contactor?

10. What is the best method of removing oil and grease from contacts and other surfaces where it might be harmful?

11. When using cleaning materials, what precautions should be taken?

12. What will be a likely result of poor adjustment of the linkage on a brake?

13. What causes a change in the timing on dashpot-type time-delay relays?

14. What two adjustments are likely to change the setting of the pull-in, drop-out, and differential currents of a current relay?

15. What is the difference between maintenance and repair as applied to control circuits and components?

9

Trouble-shooting
Control Circuits

Trouble shooting is a field of control work which generally separates the men from the boys. Many a man who can do a beautiful job of wiring a new control circuit from a circuit diagram is lost if the circuit fails to function as expected. Your chief asset in this field is an analytical mind trained in all of the aspects of control functions, components, circuits, and circuit analysis. The secret to efficient and accurate trouble shooting lies in determining the section of the control circuit that contains the trouble component and then selecting the proper component to be checked. This can only be accomplished by efficient and accurate circuit analysis, not by trial and error, long, extended wire tracing, or indiscriminate checking of components at random.

9-1 General Procedure

First let us consider a new circuit which has just been wired but fails to function as it was expected. Here there is a possibility that the wiring has been misconnected or even that the circuit was not properly designed. If we check all of the connections in all of the wiring, however, it becomes a trial-and-error process and generally involves a considerable waste of time.

The first procedure should be to analyze the circuit to determine that it has been properly designed and should work as expected if the wiring was done properly. The next step is to follow the operation of the equipment through the expected sequence until we find the section of the circuit which is not properly operating. When you have located the section of the circuit which is giving trouble, it should be simple procedure to check the wiring and operation of the components involved in this section of the circuit and clear whatever the trouble might be.

In this process you have already made use of your knowledge of analysis of circuits and your knowledge of components and their proper functions to determine whether or not they are operating as they should. Any lack of knowledge on your part of control functions, control components, control circuits, or circuit analysis will cause undue delay and wasted time in this process. When you have located the trouble in this section of the control circuit, the sequence should be started over and run through until either it has operated successfully or another section of the control circuit has been determined to be malfunctioning.

When considering trouble-shooting an existing circuit, we can generally eliminate the possibility of improper connections. If the circuit had been improperly wired, it would not have operated originally. It is surprising, however, how many men will begin their trouble-shooting procedure by checking out the wiring, connection by connection, to determine if it was properly made. This procedure is an injustice to the plant owner and the operator of the machine, who are interested in speedy and efficient repair rather than time-consuming experimentation.

The first step in trouble-shooting an existing circuit which has developed trouble is to understand that circuit and to understand the operation of the machine it controls. On complex circuits time generally does not allow the service man or trouble shooter to digest the complete circuit. With the help of the operator, however, you can determine how much of that circuit is operating. Follow the machine through its cycles until it reaches the point where it does not function properly. Having determined this point, you can analyze the circuit, starting with the section that does not operate. A careful check of this circuit and a location of the components involved in this section of the circuit will generally lead you to the source of the trouble you are seeking. The malfunction of some control component must be the cause of the circuit failure.

In the rare case where insulation breakdown is the cause of the trouble, it should be evident from a visual inspection of the components and the wiring. Quite frequently, however, a grounding of a wire in the control circuit may escape detection in a visual inspection, and if it is suspected that a ground is the cause of the trouble, careful checks should be made with the power off. With an ohmmeter determine the resistance to ground of the wires in this particular section of the control circuit.

Let us assume that you have now located the section of the control circuit which seems to be causing the trouble. The first step is to locate the components involved in this part of the circuit. There must be a coil of a relay, a contactor, or some other device which is energized by this section of the control, and the machine should be run through its sequence to determine if this coil does receive energy.

If the contactor or relay does not close as it should, the circuit should be disconnected and the wires removed from the coil of the relay or contactor so that a voltage check can be taken. Apply a voltmeter across the wires which were connected to the coil and again energize the circuit operating the control sequence up to this point. If the voltmeter indicates a proper voltage applied, then the trouble most likely is in the windings of the coil itself. Do not attempt to check the voltage or resistance of the coil while it is conencted in the circuit, since false readings are likely to result from feedback and circular paths in the control circuit.

If it is suspected that the coil is at fault, disconnect the power from the circuit and with an ohmmeter check the resistance of the coil, which should be very low on a d-c resistance check. If the coil is burnt out, you will receive a high resistance reading or a reading of infinity on the ohmmeter, indicating that the coil needs to be replaced. Do not depend on the coil smelling burnt or showing any visible evidence of being burnt out, since this is not always the case.

Suppose that our voltage check showed that the voltage did not reach the coil when it should in the sequence of operation of the control circuit. This indicates that some contact is not closing when it should, thus deenergizing the circuit to the coil. A careful study of this section of the control circuit following the principles outlined under Circuit Analysis should easily show what contacts should close in order to energize this coil. You must now locate the components which contain these contacts and again operate the machine through its sequence, observing the operation of the relay, limit switch, float switch, pressure switch, or other device that contains these contacts, to determine whether it operates mechanically as it should. If this component does operate mechanically, it indicates two possibilities. The first and most likely is that the contacts involved are not properly closing or are coated with copper oxide or other insulating material which prevents them passing current to the coil as they should. The other possibility is an open circuit due to a broken or burnt wire. This generally, however, is the least likely cause of trouble. Having checked the contacts and eliminated the trouble, which probably will be found there, again operate the control circuit with all coils connected, and if it does complete its sequence, then proceed to apply the above procedure to the next section of the control which does not function.

The above procedure is based on years of experience and an understanding of the fact that control circuits are made up basically of only two things: contacts, which make and break the circuit, and coils, which operate these contacts. If the contacts close and open as they should, then the proper voltages will be applied or disconnected from the coils as they should. If this is true, then the malfunction must lie in the coil itself. If the contacts do not operate properly, however, then the trouble must be in the contacts or in the associated wire which carries this current from the contact to the coil.

The most important rule in trouble shooting is to change only one thing at a time. If you find a set of contacts that you suspect are not properly functioning, correct this trouble and try the circuit again before changing anything else. If you find a coil you suspect to be burnt or otherwise causing trouble, repair or replace it and try the circuit again before attempting any other changes. One of the most common mistakes of trouble shooters is to change or correct several supposed troubles at one time before trying the circuit for operation. Quite frequently several changes made at one time may introduce more trouble than you had originally. This should be made a cardinal law in your work as a trouble shooter and will put you far ahead of the field in efficiency of your work. It is very seldom that several parts of a machine would wear out at the same instant. Therefore, even though the over-all condition of the control components may be poor, it still remains probable that only one component has failed completely.

If the machine that you are trouble-shooting is not thoroughly familiar to you, do not underestimate the value of the operator in your process of determining the cause of trouble. His knowledge of the normal operation of this piece of equipment can be put to work to eliminate a lot of wasted time on your part in determining how the machine should operate. Depend on him to help you locate components which may be hidden by parts of the machine, since he probably knows where they are. In short, make use of every available source of information to shorten the time necessary for you to arrive at the spot of trouble.

All failures of electric control circuits are not necessarily caused by electrical troubles. Quite frequently, the mechanical malfunction of some component may be the sole source of trouble, so remember to examine suspected components not only for electrical trouble but also for mechanical trouble.

It must also be pointed out that a man who is attempting control trouble shooting who is not equipped with a voltmeter, an ammeter, and an ohmmeter is wasting valuable time and money. He must also be trained and competent in the proper use of these instruments and the proper interpretation of the readings that they give him. Even though you may know many men who do not make use of all these instruments in their trouble-shooting work, it is an indisputable fact that their efficiency could be greatly increased by a proper understanding and application of these instruments to their work.

9-2 Trouble-shooting Control Components

All that need be said of the individual problems involved in the various components of control has been covered in Chap. 8 on maintenance of control circuits. The trouble spots recommended in this chapter for checking under maintenance procedure are identical with those trouble spots which will have to be detected in the process of trouble shooting and repairing the circuit after it has failed to perform as it should.

Again, the best equipment for efficient and proper trouble shooting of individual components is a complete knowledge of their proper operation and a familiarity with as many manufacturers' versions of each component as possible. Much of this knowledge will of necessity have to be gained through experience. The student may make a good impression on this required knowledge by a study of manufacturers' literature and by making a concerted effort to familiarize himself with the various components he comes in contact with in his daily work.

9-3 Step-by-step Procedure

In order to make the procedure outlined in Sec. 9-1 clearer to you, we shall now consider a circuit and determine the probable cause of some troubles which we shall assume to have occurred in this circuit.

The circuit of Fig. 9-1 is that of a chilled-water air conditioning compressor. The components as shown on the diagram are as follows: The coil CR is a control relay. The coil $M1$ is the starter for the chilled-water pump. The coil $M2$ is the starter for the condenser water pump. The coil $M3$ is the starter for the oil pump on the compressor itself. The coil $M4$ is the compressor motor starter. The contact identified as T is a thermostat which senses the temperature of the chilled-water return. Its function is to start the condenser water pump when this temperature reaches a predetermined

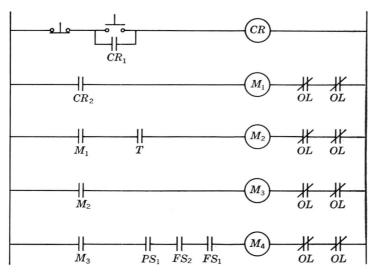

Fig. 9-1   Circuit for chilled-water air conditioning compressor control.

high level. The contact identified as $PS1$ is an oil-pressure switch whose function it is to stop the compressor should the oil pump fail and also to prevent its starting before the proper oil pressure has been obtained. The contact identified as $FS1$ is a flow switch in the chilled-water piping system. Its function is to prevent the compressor from running unless there is sufficient flow of condenser water to the condenser coil.

Suppose now that you are called in to trouble-shoot this circuit. The first step should be to determine from the owner or operator what trouble he is having with his circuit. Suppose that he tells you that the condenser water pump does not start as it should. Then from a study of a diagram we can assume that the section of the circuit for the control relay is functioning properly, that contact $CR2$ closes, and that the chilled-water pump runs as it should. Something must be wrong in the third line of our schematic diagram.

The first procedure is probably to check the overload relays and determine that they were not tripped. Having done this, we next check the thermostat to see that its contact is closed as it should be. Here it must be pointed out that determining the setting of this thermostat and the actual water temperature will indicate whether it should be open or closed. We are assuming that through the shutdown of the machine the water temperature has increased to a point that demands that these contacts be closed. Let's assume that the thermostat contacts are closed; then inspection of the starter for the chilled-water pump is indicated to determine if contact $M1$ is closing when this contactor is energized.

If our inspection of this starter shows that this contact seems to be closing properly, then the next procedure is to disconnect the wires from coil $M2$ and apply an ohmmeter to the coil to determine whether it was open or not. From the preceding analysis, it is almost certain that this coil will be found open, and for the sake of this illustration we will assume that it is. Before you replace this coil, the starter should be examined for proper mechanical operation. Determine that the contact arm which raises and lowers or swings to move the contacts is free from bind and that the spring tension is not excessive. Also examine the face of the magnetic pole pieces to see that they have not been abused and possibly damaged by someone forcing them or even through the many operations of closing of the contactor. When all mechanical problems have been eliminated, install a new coil in the starter.

It would be good practice to check the voltage at the ends of the wires which feed this coil before putting it back into service. This can be done by connecting a voltmeter between the ends of these wires and operating the control circuit up to this point. If the voltage is excessively low or excessively high, then the cause of this trouble must be determined and eliminated. Otherwise, the new coil will also burn out.

Suppose that this circuit did not malfunction in this way, but instead the report was that everything seemed to work except the compressor itself. Then our operation would be to energize the circuit and watch its sequence to determine for ourselves where it failed. We would see that the control relay operates, the chilled-water pump starts, and the condenser water pump starts, and then that the oil pump on the compressor starts.

Here we shall assume that our sequence stopped and the compressor did not come on the line as it should. Again examining our circuit, we find that we have a contact on the oil pump starter which could cause trouble. We have a pressure switch and two float switches which might be the source of trouble. So again we must determine which of these components is not properly functioning. If these components are readily accessible, a physical examination of each of them may immediately disclose the trouble. If they are inaccessible, however, a good procedure to follow is to disconnect the wires from the starter coil and operate the control circuit to determine if voltage is reaching the coil, thus eliminating the possibility of trouble being in the coil itself.

Let us assume that the contact $M3$ is properly functioning and we have checked it. The two flow switches have been determined to be properly functioning and their contacts closed. Then the examination of the pressure switch is the only remaining possibility. It may even be necessary in some cases to recalibrate pressure switches with known pressures to see that they are operating at the settings which show on their indicating dials. Again, however, the procedure is to inspect physically and determine the actual cause for the part not functioning properly.

SUMMARY

While this procedure may seem oversimplified, as you are guided through the diagram on a supposed trouble-shooting job, it is the basis upon which good trouble-shooting practice is laid.   No matter how complex the control circuit is, it can be separated into simple branches such as we have illustrated here and in other sections of this book.   The efficient trouble shooter will narrow his trouble down to one of these simple branches of even a very complex circuit, so that the actual process of locating the troublesome component will be as simple as outlined here.

REVIEW QUESTIONS

1. When is it necessary to check completely the connections of a whole control circuit?

2. Why must the wires be disconnected from a coil in order to determine accurately whether the coil winding is damaged or not?

3. Is all control-circuit trouble necessarily electrical trouble?

4. Does the fact that contacts appear to be touching indicate that the electric circuit is complete through them?

5. Why should the trouble shooter operate a machine through part of its sequence before starting to look for the trouble?

6. What are the two possible causes for repeated tripping of overload relays?

7. Should the trouble shooter try his circuit after repairing one fault or should he attempt to fix everything that seems as if it might be causing trouble before trying the circuit?

8. What are the most frequent sources of trouble in motor starters?

9. When trouble-shooting a circuit which has been operating, is it wise first to check to see if the wiring was done properly?

10. What is the chief source of failure of pilot devices such as float switches or limit switches?

11. In Fig. 9-1 what would be the most likely cause of the circuit operating only as long as the start button were held down?

12. What is the most likely source of trouble if, when we press the start button, the control relay remains energized but coil $M1$ does not pull in?

13. What would be the results if the overload relays on the circuit for coil $M2$ were to open while the compressor was running?

14. Which is generally the most difficult, finding the source of trouble or repairing the trouble after it is located?

15. Which of the above requires the most skill?

10

Principles
of Static Control

Static control is the term used to define a system of machine or process control which uses no moving parts or electric contacts. The substitution of solid-state devices for relays results in a great extension of the life expectancy of the control system.

In the previous chapters of this book we have discussed the language of control by relays and moving contact. Now it becomes necessary to convert this language into one that will apply to static control ideas.

10-1 Elements of Static Control *

The language of static control and its circuit requirements are expressed in terms of logic functions. Basically, these functions are fulfilled by four logic elements and a time delay. The elements are AND, NOT, OR, and MEMORY. Typical symbols for these elements are shown in Fig. 10-1. To obtain an output from an AND element, it is necessary to have inputs A and B and C and D all present. With an OR element, input

* Reprinted from General Electric Company Bulletin GEA6578.

A or *B* or *C* or any combination of inputs will produce an output. A NOT element is designed so that with an input *A*, an output will not occur; conversely, when input *A* is not present, an output will occur.

The MEMORY element provides a maintained output with a momentary *A* input. The output will continue after the *A* input is removed. With a momentary *B* input, the output is turned off. It is then necessary to provide another momentary

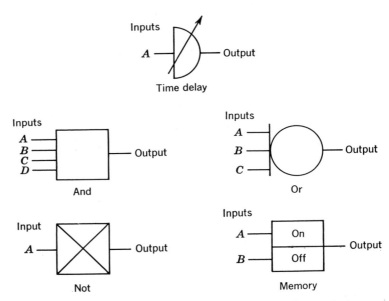

Fig. 10-1   Logic element symbols. *(General Electric Co.)*

A input before the element is turned on again. In the event of a power failure followed by a return of power, the MEMORY element will remember its last output condition (on or off) and resume operation accordingly.

In the TIME DELAY element, input *A* will result in an output after a preset period of time. The output will continue until input *A* is removed.

Any explanation of the control of a machine can be expressed in terms of the logic relationships of each function. Therefore, a control system breaks down into basic logic functions. The designer of conventional control circuits probably is not conscious of this, but examination of the progressive steps in designing a circuit will illustrate that the logic function technique was actually the method used to determine the circuit design.

For example, one of the requirements of a circuit (Fig. 10-2) might be that a solenoid $S1$ be energized when either a start

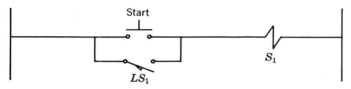

Fig. 10-2   (*General Electric Co.*)

push button is momentarily pressed or a limit switch $LS1$ is momentarily actuated. In conventional circuitry, this would be expressed as shown in Fig. 10-2. It is desirable, however, to energize $S1$ only when the start button or $LS1$ is momentarily actuated and two relays ($CR1$ and $CR2$) are picked up. Now the circuit looks like that shown in Fig. 10-3.

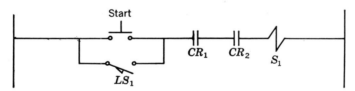

Fig. 10-3   (*General Electric Co.*)

It is also desirable to have $S1$ remain energized until another limit switch ($LS2$) is actuated. When power is restored after a failure, the circuit must remember its condition of output before the failure occurred and resume operation at the same point in the cycle where it left off. The new circuit (Fig. 10-4) now includes a mechanically held relay ($CL1$ pickup coil and $CU1$ dropout coil). A further requirement is that $S1$ should be deenergized only when both $LS2$ is actuated and a third relay ($CR3$) is not picked up. The circuit with this added condition is shown in Fig. 10-5.

The entire operation may be summarized as follows: $S1$ will be energized when either the start button or $LS1$ is momentarily actuated and $CR1$ and $CR2$ are picked up. $S1$ remains energized until both $LS2$ is actuated and $CR3$ is not picked up.

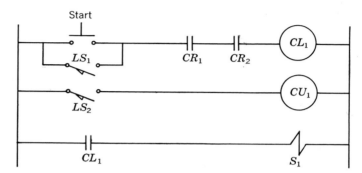

Fig. 10-4   (General Electric Co.)

When power is restored after a failure, the circuit must *remember* (MEMORY) its output condition and resume operation at the same point in the cycle where it left off.

An examination of the above summary shows that the circuit

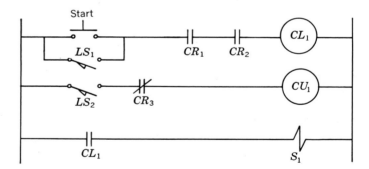

Fig. 10-5   (General Electric Co.)

design was based on the use of logic functions. An explanation of the circuit may now be expressed in terms of logic elements.

To energize $S1$, the start button or $LS1$ must first be momentarily energized. Therefore, a two-input OR element is the first requirement of the logic function circuit (Fig. 10-6).   Before $S1$ can be energized, however, it is necessary to actuate the start button or $LS1$ and pick up $CR1$ and $CR2$. A three-input AND element, utilizing the $CR1$ and $CR2$ inputs

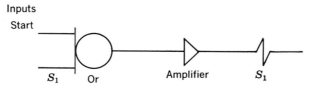

Fig. 10-6   (*General Electric Co.*)

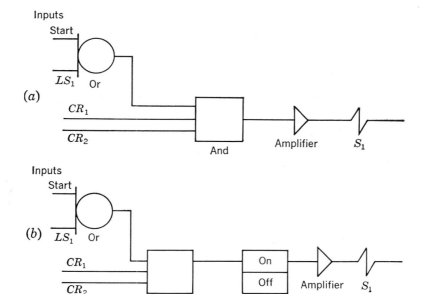

Fig. 10-7   (*General Electric Co.*)

instead of the relays, plus the output from the OR element, will perform this function as shown in Fig. 10-7a.

To keep $S1$ energized until it is desirable to deenergize it, a continued input to $S1$ is required.   A MEMORY element will accomplish this function.   Since the MEMORY element retains an output after the input signal has been removed, $S1$ will

remain energized until an OFF input is introduced in the circuit
(Fig. 10-7b). To deenergize S1, two conditions must be fulfilled: $CR3$ must not be picked up, and $LS2$ must be actuated.
Therefore, two additional logic elements are required: a single-
input NOT element that will produce an output when the $CR3$
input, instead of the relay, is not present, and a two-input AND
element that feeds into the OFF input of the MEMORY element
when an input is present from both $LS2$ and the NOT element
(Fig. 10-8).

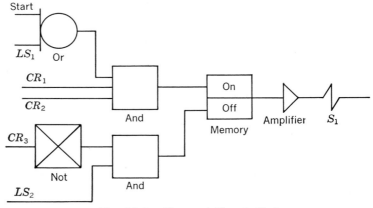

Fig. 10-8   (*General Electric Co.*)

The final requirement, that the circuit must remember its
condition of output upon the return of power after an interruption, is also fulfilled by the MEMORY element. This element retains the last signal (ON or OFF) that was fed into it
even after the input signal has been removed. A completed
logic element circuit may now be drawn. The functions of
$CR1$, $CR2$, $CR3$, and $CL1$, as employed in this part of the
conventional circuit, have been performed by logic elements.

From the above discussion it should be obvious that in order
to have an output from an AND unit, you must have input
voltage present at input 1, input 2, and input 3 for a three-
input AND unit. The two-input OR unit requires only an
input voltage at one or the other of its two inputs. The NOT
element has an output whenever there is not an input voltage

present at its input terminal or terminals. The MEMORY element maintains an output or no output in response to momentary inputs to either its on or off section.

There are a variety of ways to accomplish static control, a few of which we shall consider. The oldest concept is that of using vacuum tubes, and they might well be used except for the disadvantages that they are subject to filament burnout and aging, are bulky and fragile, and require considerable filament power.

Transistors offer a small package, low power consumption, complete static operation, and long life. The chief disadvantage to transistors lies in the lack of tolerance control in their manufacture. Because of this lack of quality control most manufacturers of static control systems have avoided the use of transistors in their logic elements. The rapid developments in transistor manufacture, however, are making them more and more desirable as the basic component to be used in logic elements.

Most static control systems employ, as their basic unit, magnetic amplifiers of the self-saturating type. These magnetic units are used in conjunction with rectifiers, capacitors, and resistors. They give completely reliable static operation and long trouble-free life.

10-2 Why Static Control *

The subject of control can be broken down into three parts: information, decision, and action. Specifically, the information section of a machine is comprised of its sensing devices, such as limit switches, push buttons, pressure switches, temperature sensors, and other devices that can receive and transmit information which is pertinent to the control.

Once we have information, we must assimilate and correlate it in order to arrive at a decision to do something. This portion of the control is called the *decision* portion, or the "brains" of the control.

Once a decision has been reached, we must take action in terms of operating a solenoid valve, a contactor or starter, an

* Reprinted from General Electric Company Bulletin GPC-B18.

indicating light, or some other device that will produce the desired result.

Static control, as we know it today, performs the decision-making portion of the over-all control. Normally, the decision-making portion has been accomplished by means of machine-tool and other types of relays, but because of our rapid strides toward automation, these devices in many applications are not altogether satisfactory. As we approach automation, we tie more machines together to form a continuous process. As such, the control becomes considerably more complex because we not only control the individual machines, but also have to coordinate material transfer between them, as well as perform certain interlocking functions. As a result of this complexity, the reliability of each control device becomes increasingly important. It is self-evident that if a device malfunctions on a panel containing 200 relays, finding trouble will be considerably more difficult than if there were only four relays on the panel.

Also, automation increases productivity, causing higher and higher duty cycles on the control devices themselves. A few years ago a machine-tool relay life of 10 million operations was considered to be entirely adequate. Today a life of 20 to 25 million operations is not adequate for many applications. Therefore, the need for control devices whose life is independent of the number of operations they perform is growing daily. The ability to operate controls in different environments is being desired more and more, particularly in chemical and food-process automation.

Static control seems to be the best method of achieving the three main objectives we have discussed. Magnetic amplifiers and other static devices have in common a characteristic of operation which is basically different from that of relays. This difference is that static devices may have one or more inputs and a single output. Relays, on the other hand, have a single input (to the coil) and one or more outputs, depending on the number of contacts used. Therefore, a different approach must be used in designing control schemes using static devices. The computer people were faced with the same prob-

lems a number of years ago, when they had to convey information by use of vacuum tubes. They devised a means of
assimilating information and arriving at decisions by a system
of logic functions. They showed that all intelligence could be
broken down into five basic logic functions, each having one
or more inputs and a single output.

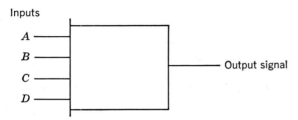

Fig. 10-9   The AND function. All inputs to an AND function must be present to establish and maintain the output.   (*General Electric* Co.)

10-3   Theory of Logic Function *

The first logic function is the AND function (Fig. 10-9).
The AND function, as shown, means that input *A, and* input
B, and input *C, and* input *D* must be present to establish and

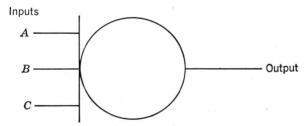

Fig. 10-10   The OR function. Any input or any combination of inputs
must be present to establish and maintain an output. (*General Electric* Co.)

maintain an output. Loss of any one or more signals will
immediately stop the output. Summarizing, we can say that
all inputs to an AND function must be present to establish and
maintain an output.

* Reprinted from General Electric Company Bulletin GPC-B18.

The next logic function is the OR function (Fig. 10-10). The OR function will produce an output if either input *A, or* input *B, or* input *C,* or any combination of *A, B,* and *C* is present. Summarizing again, we can say that if *any* input or *any combination* of inputs is present, an output will be produced.

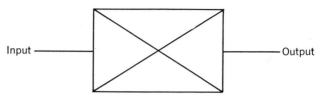

Fig. 10-11   The NOT function. An input will not produce an output. Conversely, no input will produce an output. (*General Electric* Co.)

The third logic function is the NOT function (Fig. 10-11). The NOT function is tricky in that if it does *not* have an input, it will have an output. Conversely, if an input is present, the NOT function will *not* have an output.

The fourth major function is that of MEMORY. It does just what the term implies: it remembers a signal. The basic

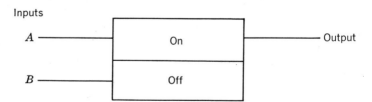

Fig. 10-12   The basic memory function. A momentary input to the ON section will produce a maintained output. A momentary input to the OFF section will cause the output, if present, to stop. (*General Electric* Co.)

MEMORY function (Fig. 10-12) operates so that a momentary input to the ON section will produce a maintained output. A momentary input to the OFF section will cause the output, if present, to stop. The MEMORY function can be designed to produce certain desired characteristics. The *retentive memory* (Fig. 10-13) is a basic memory with the added capability of always remembering its output state when system power is interrupted and later restored. The *off-return memory* (Fig. 10-14) is a basic memory with the added capability of always returning to the OFF condition when system power is interrupted and later restored.

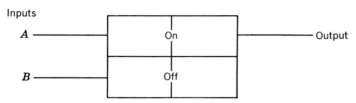

Fig. 10-13 The retentive memory function. The retentive memory is a basic memory with the added capability of always remembering its output state when the system power is interrupted and later restored. (*General Electric* Co.)

The fifth and last basic logic function is the DELAY function (Fig. 10-15). This is merely a time delay so constructed that a maintained input will produce an output after an intentional time delay. Since the time delay may be varied continuously over its range, an arrow is placed through the *D* to indicate that it is adjustable.

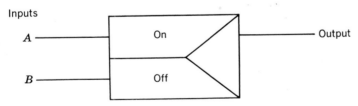

Fig. 10-14 The off-return memory function. The off-return memory is a basic memory with the added capability of always returning to the OFF condition when the system power is interrupted and later restored. (*General Electric* Co.)

To keep the size, weight, and expense of magnetic amplifier logic functions to a reasonable value, they are constructed so that they handle only very small amounts of power, and their output is considerably less than 1 watt. Therefore, when a signal output shows that a decision has been made to take action, it is necessary to amplify this signal into usable power to actuate the controlled device. The logic symbol for the amplifier is shown in Fig. 10-16.

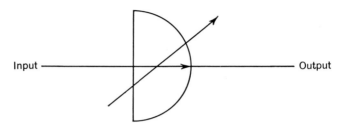

Input ——————————————— Output

Fig. 10-15   The delay function. A maintained input will produce an output after an intentional time delay. (*General Electric* Co.)

10-4   Application of Static Elements *

Now we have our tools. Let's see how they are used. Suppose it is our desire to control a planer table which is operated as shown in Fig. 10-17. It is desired to oscillate the table back and forth by means of a reversing motor. For example,

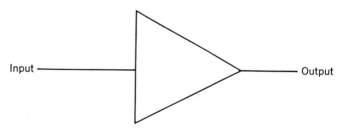

Input ——————————————— Output

Fig. 10-16   The amplifier. An amplifier converts an output signal from a logic element to a larger power output required to actuate the controlled device. (*General Electric* Co.)

if the right traverse contactor is actuated, the table will be driven to the right. When the right operating limit switch is actuated, it is desired to have the right traverse contactor deenergized and the left traverse contactor operated so that the table is driven to the left until it hits the left operating limit switch. It is also desired to have certain protective controls

* Reprinted from General Electric Company Bulletin GPC-B18.

as well as direction from the machine operator. The protective controls wanted are motor overload protection, interlocking with the coolant supply, and minimum lube pressure.

Let's first set up the continuous oscillating motion by means of logic functions. In this case, we have the right traverse contactor solenoid and the left traverse contactor solenoid to operate. Let's put them down with their respective amplifiers (Fig. 10-18). Logically speaking, when the right traverse amplifier is actuated, we do not wish to operate the left traverse amplifier, so our input to the right traverse amplifier should

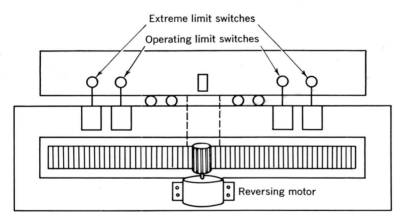

Fig. 10-17   Planer table. (*General Electric Co.*)

also be fed to a NOT element driving the left traverse amplifier. To operate the right traverse amplifier, we must next look at the character of the incoming information.

When the table actuates the left operating limit switch, the right traverse amplifier is actuated. When the right traverse amplifier is actuated, however, the table is driven away from the left operating limit switch. Therefore, it can be seen that the limit switch operation is of a momentary nature and that the table control must remember the direction to be traveled until the opposite limit switch is actuated. Since memory is required, we shall turn on a MEMORY element with the momentary input and drive the right traverse solenoid amplifier and the NOT element from its maintained output.

Now the table progresses from the left side until it operates the right operating limit switch. At this point we want to achieve two things. First, we want to turn off the right traverse amplifier and, secondly, we want to energize the left traverse amplifier. In this case, both requirements can be achieved by merely using the right operating limit switch to turn off the MEMORY, which stops the output to the right traverse amplifier and to the NOT element. With no input to the NOT element, we produce an output from the NOT element which drives the left traverse solenoid, and the table is actuated to the left to complete the cycle.

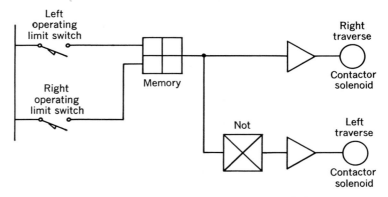

Fig. 10-18   Planer-table circuit, step 1. (*General Electric* Co.)

Let's add next the additional controls required with this machine. First we would like two modes of operation; either running continuously or jogging. Referring to Fig. 10-19, let's put in a start button in series to one input of a two-input AND. Since the stop button and the extreme limit switches are of the normally closed variety, we can put them in series to the second input of the two-input AND. Therefore, when the start button is pressed, an output will be present from the two-input AND. It is not our desire, however, to have the operator stand at the control panel with his finger on the start button at all times. To overcome this difficulty, we shall take the output and feed it back into the same input used by the start button. Hence, once an output has been established, the operator can release the start button and the output will be maintained, since a two-input AND is now sealed in, very much like a relay which has been sealed in by one of its own normally open contacts. This output will, of course, signify direction by the operator for continuous running.

It is now desired either to run continuously or to jog. To accomplish this, we shall use an OR element with one input from the output of the two-input AND and the other input

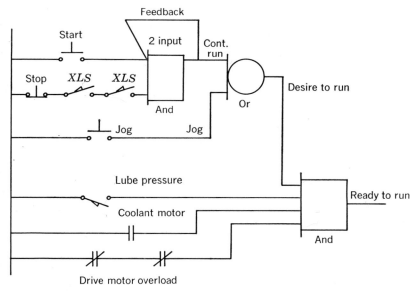

Fig. 10-19   Planer-table circuit, step 2. *(General Electric Co.)*

from a jog button. The output of the OR element shows a desire on the part of the operator to run the machine as long as he holds his finger on the jog button.

Next, we wish to incorporate the protective functions. For this situation we wish to combine the desires of the operator to run and to have a minimum lube pressure. We also wish him to have the coolant motor operating and the drive-motor overload relays incorporated into the circuit. These signals are added by means of a four-input AND, the output of which signifies "ready to run."

The oscillating portion is combined with the manual and protective functions, as shown in Fig. 10-20.

The circuit is now virtually complete except for two things. For jogging operations and the start up, it may be desired to

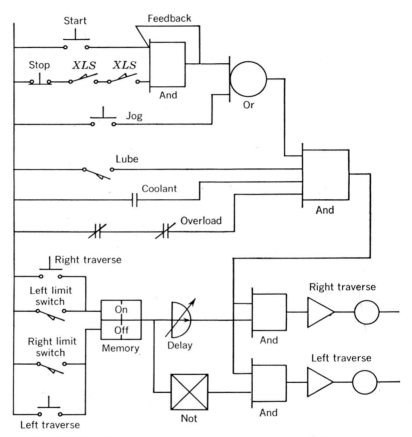

Fig. 10-20   Planer-table circuit, complete. *(General Electric Co.)*

be sure the table starts in the particular direction desired by the operator. The direction can be easily selected by presetting the MEMORY (on or off) by means of push buttons in parallel with the left and right limit switches. Also, if the table is required to stop at one end of its travel in order to blow off chips, a DELAY function could be put in the automatic cycle portion as shown.   This completes the desired operating cycle requirements.

SUMMARY

The basic functions of static control are four logic elements, AND, OR, NOT, and MEMORY, and a time delay.   The three parts of a static control system are information, decision, and action.   An example of static control described in this chapter is a planer table.

REVIEW QUESTIONS

1. Basically, what is static control?
2. What are the four basic logic elements?
3. Draw the symbols for each of the four basic logic elements.
4. The ~~memory~~ element provides a maintained output with a momentary input.

11

Static Control
Systems

Each company that makes static control systems uses its own ideas as to how to accomplish a desired result. We shall take up only three of these ideas, two in this chapter and one in the next, to show the similarity and differences.

11-1   The General Electric Static Control System *

Now that we have seen how logic elements are used in their application to control circuits, let us see how they operate as devices. First of all, let's assume that we have a typical logic element in front of us and that for the present it has one input and one output. For the moment, do not consider what happens inside the logic element, but merely what happens to the output when an input is applied. Since our logic elements are essentially d-c devices, our input signals can be either negative or positive, although our output is always positive. If we were to put into the logic element a strong negative signal

* Reprinted with permission of the General Electric Company General Purpose Control Department (also Secs. 11-2, 11-3, and 11-4).

and gradually change our input so that we went from a minus input through zero to a plus input, measuring the output at the same time, we could plot a curve that would look something like that shown in Fig. 11-1. This produces a rather unusual curve, but it is just the thing we need to perform various logic functions.

With no alteration, we immediately have a NOT function, as can be seen by referring to Fig. 11-2. Remember at this point our definition of a NOT element, which says that with no

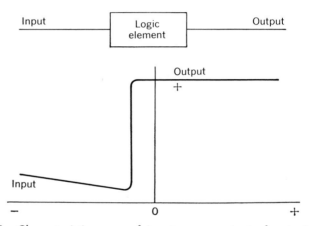

Fig. 11-1   Characteristic curve of input versus output of a typical logic element. (*General Electric Co.*)

input the output is in the ON zone and with an input the output is in the OFF zone. With zero input on the curve, we are in the ON zone, but if a negative signal is applied to the input, the output drops to the OFF zone.

To obtain another function, we shall build into our logic element a negative signal, or bias, as it is usually called. Bias will hold our output in the OFF zone with no external signal applied, as shown in Fig. 11-3. Any external signal applied in the positive direction will cause the output to go from OFF to ON. Because these are magnetic amplifier devices, it is possible to have multiple inputs. Consequently, by the use of more windings, we can turn on this element with input *A*, or input *B*, or input *C*, or any combination of *A, B,* and *C*. This

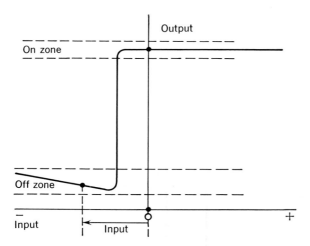

Fig. 11-2 NOT element characteristic curve. With no input, the output is in the ON zone. With an input, the output is in the OFF zone. (*General Electric* Co.)

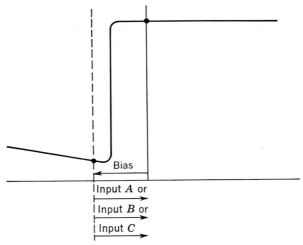

Fig. 11-3 OR element characteristic curve. With no input, the output is in the OFF zone. (*General Electric* Co.)

fits the description of the OR element, that any input or any combination of inputs can produce an output.

To obtain the MEMORY function, we alter the output characteristic curve somewhat (Fig. 11-4). If we took a characteristic curve of the MEMORY element, working from minus through zero to plus, we would follow the same curve as that for the NOT and OR element. If, however, we proceed to take the characteristic curve from plus through zero to minus, something else happens. Working back, we begin to retrace the

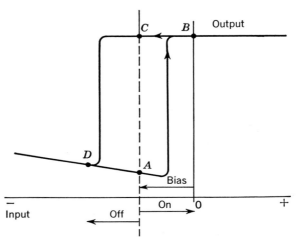

Fig. 11-4 Memory element characteristic curve. Momentary inputs will produce sustained output states. (*General Electric Co.*)

original curve until the point is reached where the element would be expected to drop to the OFF state. The element remains in the ON condition, however, even though our input is very negative. With a strong enough negative signal, the input finally drops down to the OFF condition and begins to retrace the curve of the original.

If we bias this element, with no external signal applied, the output is at point *A*. If we apply an ON signal, the output is driven from *A* to *B*. If the ON signal is removed, the output cannot come directly back to *A,* since this is strictly a one-way path. Instead, the output goes from *B* to *C,* where it is held by the bias. Now we have the condition of the element having full output with no externally applied signal, and therefore it has remembered a momentary input. To turn the element off, it is necessary only to apply an OFF signal in a negative direction. The output then goes from C to D. Removing the OFF signal causes the output to go from D to A, back to where we started.

The AND element and the DELAY element operating principles can be better seen after we get a little into the circuitry.

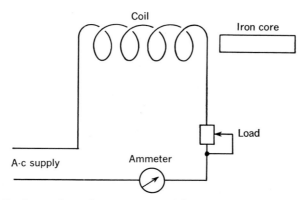

Fig. 11-5 Basic idea of magnetic amplifiers—1. (*General Electric Co.*)

11-2 The Magnetic Amplifier

To understand the operation of our logic system, we must first understand the basic idea of a magnetic amplifier. Perhaps you are already familiar with the principles involved. Just in case you are not, we shall venture a crude explanation which will be sufficient. Suppose we had a coil of wire which was connected to a load of some sort and in turn connected to an ammeter, as shown in Fig. 11-5. If we connected the two leads to an a-c supply, we could adjust the load so that a full-scale deflection on the ammeter would be required.

If we were to take an iron bar of some sort and insert it in the middle of the open coil (Fig. 11-6), what would happen to to the reading on the ammeter? The reading would drop, of course, because of the magnetic effect on the iron core. The reason for this effect, of course, is that current through the coil of wire causes a flux change in and around the iron. This, in turn, induces a large counter emf in the coil which reduces the load current by a considerable amount. Here we have a crude switch, that is, one without contacts. This switch is not static,

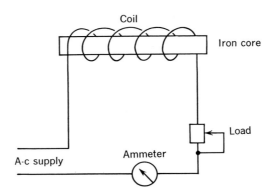

Fig. 11-6   Basic idea of magnetic amplifiers—2. (*General Electric Co.*)

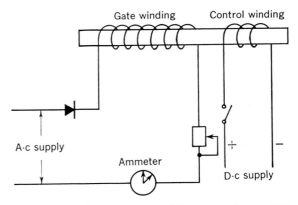

Fig. 11-7   Basic idea of magnetic amplifiers—3. (*General Electric Co.*)

however, because to make the output current go up and down, the iron core must be moved in and out. Since we need a completely static switch we must resort to an additional gimmick. If we could just make the iron look at times like air (magnetically speaking) and at other times make the iron act like iron, then we would have achieved a static contactless switch. This can be done by the addition of a d-c winding (Fig. 11-7), which is so wound that when energized it will drive the iron to magnetic saturation and effectively make the iron bar act as if it were out of the circuit.

Thus, we have the basic idea of a magnetic amplifier: current through the main or gate winding is controlled by the state of the iron core within the gate winding, and the state of the

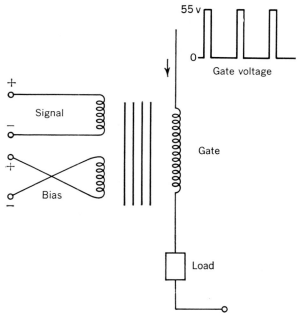

Fig. 11-8 Practical magnetic amplifier. (*General Electric* Co.)

iron core is controlled by means of a d-c winding. We shall see how the same principles are applied in the design of our logic element.

11-3 Design of Logic Elements

In Fig. 11-8 we have rearranged the components somewhat although we have not changed the basic idea. We have again a gate winding, a load, an iron core, and a signal winding.

Since most of our elements require an internal negative signal, or bias, we shall put it in. Because the bias signal is always negative and we prefer to work with positive currents, we can show it as a negative signal by simply reversing the direction of current through the winding on the coil, as shown in Fig. 11-8.

To understand the operation, we shall begin by making some assumptions. First, let us assume there is no signal present on the signal winding. Second, we shall assume the bias is always energized with direct current and that the iron is initially not positively saturated.

Now let us apply gate voltage. As seen in the figure, the gate voltage consists of narrow positive d-c pulses applied at the top of gate winding. When the gate voltage is applied, the first pulse of current goes down through the gate winding. Since the core was not in positive saturation, however, a large back emf was induced in the gate winding, which limited the current through the gate winding and through the load to a small magnetizing current. The first pulse did accomplish one thing, however; it succeeded in driving the iron core almost to positive saturation.

The effect of the bias now makes itself felt between the end of the first pulse and the beginning of the next pulse, and it acts in such a manner that it drives the core to negative saturation, essentially undoing the work of the first pulse. The action of the bias in driving the core to negative saturation is called *resetting*. Consequently, with no signal applied, the pulse of gate voltage tries to drive the core into positive saturation. Between pulses the bias acts to reset the core, with the net result that no appreciable current flows down through load.

If a signal is applied, however, we obtain a different condition. As soon as a signal is applied, the gate pulse immediately drives the core toward positive saturation as before. The effect of a signal, however, is that of nullifying or neutralizing the effect of the bias signal so that the bias cannot reset the core. Therefore, when the following gate pulse comes along, the core completes its saturation, the impedance of the gate drops to approximately 10 per cent of its previous value, a relatively high current flows in the load, and we have an output. As soon as the signal is removed, the bias resets the core, the action continues just as before the signal was applied, and the signal output stops.

To make a magnetic amplifier operate correctly, we have to use a very special core material called *square-loop* core material. This metal is a mixture of nickel and iron which has been processed in a very particular manner to give it desirable characteristics. If we were to build a logic element, as shown previously, with transformer iron, we would not get the desired

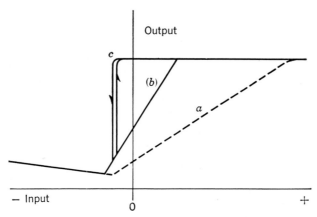

Fig. 11-9   Characteristic curves of amplifiers made with core of transformer iron (a), square-loop core material (b), and square-loop core material plus positive feedback (c). (*General Electric Co.*)

digital output-versus-input curve as shown previously. Instead, it would look something like the dotted line (a) in Fig. 11-9. By using square-loop core material, we improve our output curve considerably, although there is still an analog portion, as shown in the b portion of the curve. We are in the switching business, however, and cannot live even with a small analog portion. We must have a digital on-and-off characteristic (*c*) if our system is to operate as desired.   Consequently, we must resort to special circuitry as shown in Fig. 11-10.

Here we have essentially the same circuit as we had before plus an additional winding, called a *feedback* winding, and a capacitor.   This is how it works: Let us assume that we just turned on an input signal.   The first pulse comes down from the gate winding and drives the core almost to saturation. Since the bias is neutralized by the effect of the signal present, the core remains very close to saturation.   The second pulse now comes through the gate, and a small current immediately

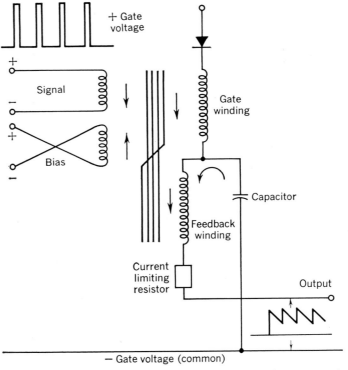

Fig. 11-10   Practical magnetic amplifier, with feedback. (*General Electric Co.*)

begins to flow down through the gate winding, feedback winding, and load, since the core was about 80 per cent positively saturated.   The effect of a small current down through the feedback winding, which is wound around the same iron core, is such that it adds to the saturation of the core and immediately drives the core to complete saturation. The net result is that the output load current goes from the very low value to full output almost instantaneously.

At the same time the output current began to flow, the capacitor was also charged by the second pulse. At the end of the second pulse, the capacitor discharges in a path (shown by the arrow) through the feedback winding and the current limiting resistor to the output. The capacitor is prevented from discharging back through the gate winding by a diode, which is shown at the top of the gate.

The effect of the capacitor is as follows: By discharging the capacitor between pulses, our final output now appears as a sawtooth voltage, which is essentially direct current with a ripple. Hence, we come into our signal winding with direct current. The output is now a plus direct current, and, even though a ripple is present, it is certainly good enough to use as a driving signal for succeeding elements. In discharging back through the feedback winding, we essentially create an

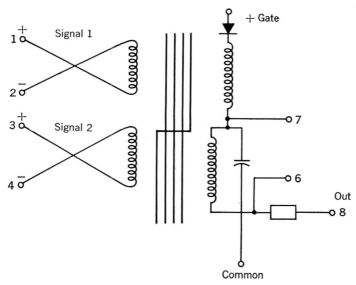

Fig. 11-11 NOT element, schematic diagram. (*General Electric Co.*)

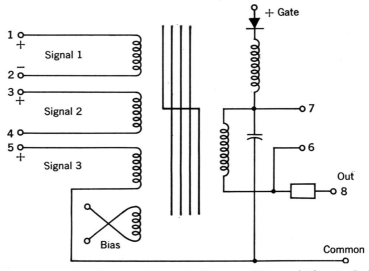

Fig. 11-12   OR element, schematic diagram. (*General Electric Co.*)

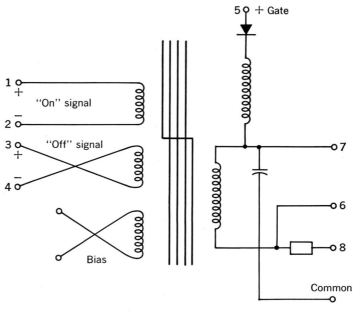

Fig. 11-13   Retentive memory element, schematic diagram. (*General Electric Co.*)

additional signal which tends to hold the core in positive saturation. The effect is that instead of our having the output drop on the analog portion of the curve shown in *b* in Fig. 11-9, when the signal is removed, it now requires a strong negative, or bias, signal to drive the output to the off condition. This accomplishes the digital OFF function, which we desire just as much as a digital ON function.

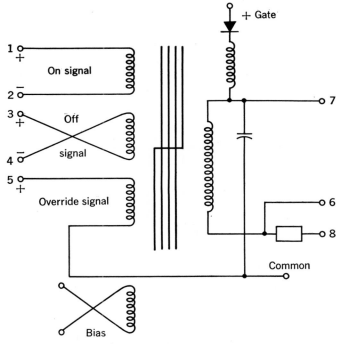

Fig. 11-14 Release memory element, schematic diagram. (*General Electric Co.*)

This design approach also reaps another benefit. If we were to increase the number of feedback turns by a large number, the turn-on would be just as it was before, but the effect of the capacitor discharging through the very large feedback winding would require an extremely strong negative signal to turn off the output. The resulting effect is the characteristic curve shown in Fig. 11-9. As can be seen, this is the basic curve by which we derive our MEMORY function.

With these fundamentals in mind, it can be readily seen how the NOT (Fig. 11-11), the OR (Fig. 11-12), and the MEMORY (Figs. 11-13 and 11-14) elements operate. The primary difference between the retentive and the off-return memories is that gate power is applied at the same time as bias power to

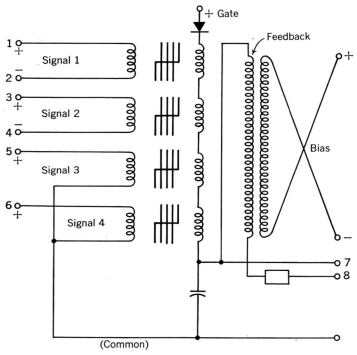

Fig. 11-15   Four-input AND schematic diagram. (*General Electric Co.*)

the retentive memory and that bias power is established before gate power in the off-return memory.

To obtain a dependable AND function, the gate and bias windings are wound around a number of cores, and each core has its individual signal winding (see Figs. 11-15, 11-16, and 11-17). To achieve an output through the load, all four cores must be driven to saturation, which means that all four signals must be present. This arrangement makes it possible to operate with utmost reliability even if overtolerance signals are

present because, after all, once a core has been driven to saturation, additional current in the signal wiring will have no effect.

Let's tackle the DELAY next (Fig. 11-18). Here we see a
difference in configuration. This device has two magnetic
cores, two gate windings, and a mutual linking winding which
is common to both cores. The gate pulses alternate between
the no. 1 and the no. 2 gates, in such a way that first a pulse is

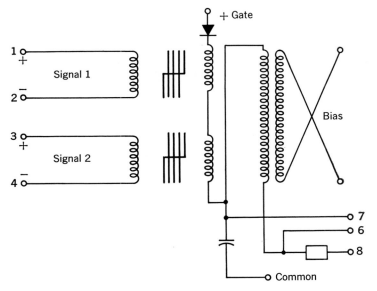

Fig. 11-16   Two-input AND schematic diagram. (*General Electric Co.*)

fed to the no. 1 gate, the next pulse goes into the no. 2 gate,
then back to no. 1, and so on. Each gate winding is so constructed that each pulse going through it will drive its respective core only a small percentage toward saturation, as
contrasted to the gate windings of the other elements, in which
one pulse would drive its core into almost complete saturation.

Referring to Fig. 11-18, we can see that, if a pulse in the no.
1 gate causes a flux change on the no. 1 core, a voltage will be
induced (and a current) in the mutual linking winding. The
linking winding is so wound that when a voltage is induced as
a result of a flux change in the no. 1 core, it causes a flux change

in the no. 2 core, which drives the no. 2 toward negative saturation. Summarizing, the effect of the pulse on the no. 1 gate
is such that it drives the no. 1 core a small percentage toward
positive saturation, while, through the linking winding, it
drives the no. 2 core back toward negative saturation.

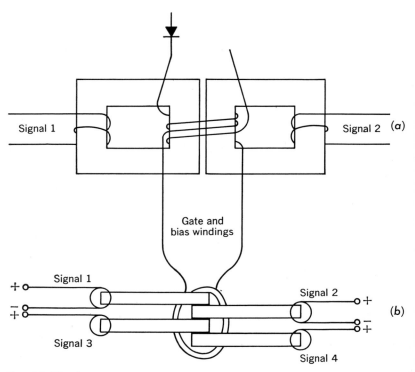

Fig. 11-17   (a) Two-input AND. (b) Four-input AND. (General Electric
Co.)

Conversely, when the following pulse comes through the
no. 2 gate winding, it tries to drive its core a small percentage
toward positive saturation, while, through the mutual linking
winding, it tries to drive the no. 1 core toward negative saturation. If the mutual linking winding had no resistance and no
losses, the two cores would buck each other indefinitely and
neither would ever become saturated. We can, however, in
creating a loss in the mutual linking winding by inserting a

potentiometer, vary the amount of resetting action and eventually achieve saturation of both cores.

In Fig. 11-19 we can get a better idea of what happens inside each core. Here we show a *B-H* curve, which is simply a curve showing saturation versus magnetizing force. We shall assume the core is initially in negative saturation at point *A*.

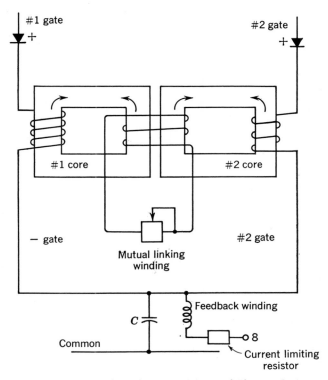

Fig. 11-18 Delay element. (*General Electric Co.*)

The first pulse drives the no. 1 core partially toward positive saturation, which leaves the core at a point of saturation shown at *B*. The effect of the second pulse coming through the no. 2 core and inducing a current in the mutual linking winding now makes itself evident. The induced voltage partially resets the no. 1 core, as shown, from *B* to *C*. The no. 1 gate receives the next pulse, which drives the core further toward positive saturation, at the conclusion of which the state of the core is shown at point D. The following pulse is applied to the no. 2 gate. This, of course, drives to partially reset the no. 1 core. In this manner, the core is gradually driven to saturation, at which time the gate conducts load current.

The control and bias winding arrangement on the delay element is quite different from that on the other elements we have discussed (see Fig. 11-20). The reason for this difference

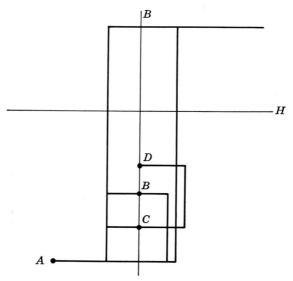

Fig. 11-19   No. 1 core saturation curves. (*General Electric Co.*)

is that the bias must be completely removed from the cores, so that only the gate pulses themselves will determine the saturation and reset of each core. This is accomplished by using the control input as a blocking voltage to stop current from going through the bias winding. The standard bias supply is not used. Instead, the bias is supplied from the 125-volt d-c original input power, which is brought in at terminal 3. This is how it works: The bias is removed by applying a control input to terminals 1 or 2, which gives a voltage drop across resistor C. This voltage appears at the blocking rectifier, causing the bias current to flow through the Zener diode, and thus allowing the element to turn on as explained above.

The Zener diode is a device that will block current in the reverse direction until a certain voltage is reached, approximately 4 volts. At this voltage the Zener-diode portion of the

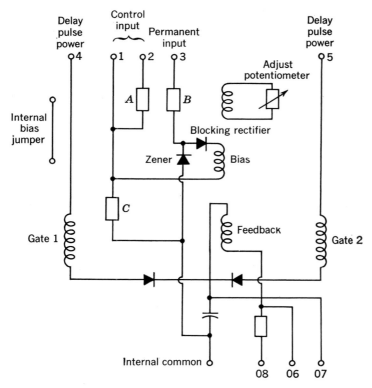

Fig. 11-20   Delay element, schematic diagram. (*General Electric Co.*)

circuit is required to provide an alternate path for the bias current. The reason is simply that when the bias current has been blocked out, the voltage at the top of the bias winding does not try to reach the 125-volt d-c bias supply voltage. The Zener diode merely provides an alternate path for the current, which holds the voltage drop across resistor B at a relatively constant value.

11-4   The Power Supply

The last major component in our logic control system is the power supply. This unit supplies all power required to operate the logic elements as well as the original input power. Input to the power supply is 110 volts 60 cycles a-c. We shall develop the power supply insteps, the first of which is shown in Fig. 11-21. A reactor is shown in series with an impedance which we shall call Z. The reactor has a saturable core and is so designed that as the voltage across it (A to B) rises, the

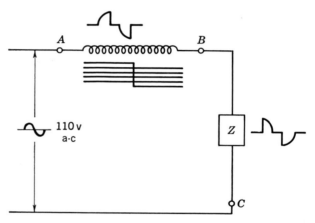

Fig. 11-21   Power supply, step 1. (*General Electric Co.*)

core will saturate near the peak of the sine wave. When the core saturates, the impedance between A and B drops almost to zero, and likewise so does the voltage. The resulting waveshape of the voltage between A and B is shown above the reactor symbol. The waveshape of the voltage across the impedance Z is then equal to the difference between the applied voltage waveshape (the pure sine wave) and the voltage drop between A and B, since the sum of the instantaneous voltage drops around the circuit has to equal the instantaneous applied voltage.

Now let us take a closer look at that impedance Z. In Fig. 11-22 we have broken it down into a second reactor and an impedance which we shall call Z'. The second reactor, which is shown between B and D, has a smaller core and is wound so that the core will saturate very quickly. As the applied voltage between B and C starts with a very steep wave front, the core between B and D has a high voltage immediately applied across it and consequently saturates very quickly. The resulting waveshape of the voltage between B and D is a series of alternating sharp voltage spikes, or pulses. These pulses are extracted from the circuit by making the small reactor between B and D a small saturable transformer, as shown on

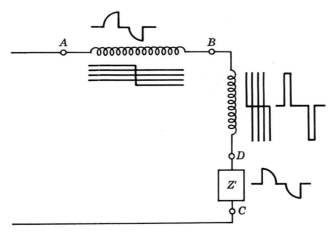

Fig. 11-22 Power supply, step 2. (*General Electric* Co.)

Fig. 11-23. The secondary of the transformer is center-tapped and rectifiers inserted as shown to make a full-wave rectifier, which essentially doubles the frequency of the output pulses.

Now let's replace the Z' in the circuit with a full-wave rectifier. All the individual bias windings for all the elements served by the power supply are placed in a series with the rectifier output. By this means we achieve our fail-safe bias system. This is how it works: If we were to lose bias power for any or all of our elements, that element would turn on, since the bias controls the resetting action on the core. Consequently, for fail-safeness it is to our advantage to shut down the entire system should failure occur. Effectively, we have placed the bias windings in series with our gate supply when we inserted the rectifier and bias in place of Z'. If any of the bias windings open up, the gate pulses are also interrupted.

In the bias portion of the power supply, there is also a choke and a capacitor for filtering purposes. An adjustable resistor is put in series with the bias winding, so that the bias current can be adjusted to the proper value for a specific number of logic elements.

Also in series with the bias windings is, of all things, a relay coil. Naturally we are immediately besieged with questions

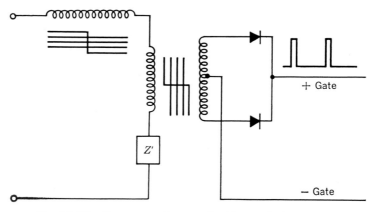

Fig. 11-23   Power supply, step 3. (*General Electric Co.*)

as to why we have a relay in the heart of a static system. Please be assured there is a very good reason for this. This bias relay has two contacts, one of which is put in series with the pulse power output, as shown in Fig. 11-24. This arrangement assures that bias is established to the logic element before gate pulses are applied when the system is first energized. This arrangement protects against the possibility of an undesired half-cycle output under certain conditions. This condition could arise whenever system power is interrupted and certain elements are in the ON condition at the time of interruption. If system power is to be restored so that a pulse or two can be generated before the bias can build up enough to reset the core, then an output can occur for a short period of

time.   The bias relay gives us protection against this possibility.   Also, if one of the rectifiers in the bias circuit should
short out, the bias relay could not pick up and pulse power
could not be applied.

The other contact of the bias relay is used for connecting
more than one power supply, so that if bias in the elements
supplied by one power supply fails, the whole system can be
shut down.   Undervoltage protection is also achieved in the
same circuit.

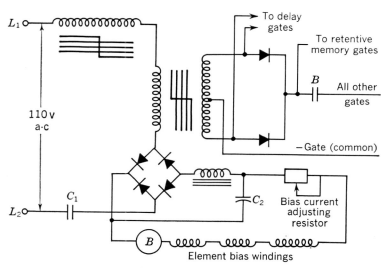

Fig. 11-24   Power supply, step 4. (*General Electric Co.*)

Capacitor $C1$ is inserted in series with the gate and the power
supply to improve the shape of the gate pulse by using the
principle of ferroresonance.

The complete power supply is shown in Fig. 11-25.   A full-
wave rectifier has been added across the line to supply original
input power.   This rectifier has an output of about 125 volts
a-c.   This power is applied across limit switches, push buttons,
and other pilot devices and is then converted into a signal of
proper voltage and current through resistor-divider networks
known as *original inputs*.

As can be seen in Fig. 11-26, the pilot contact is inserted

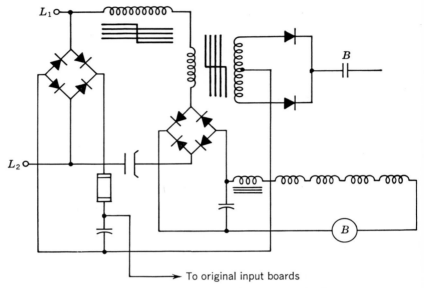

To original input boards

Fig. 11-25 Complete power supply. (*General Electric Co.*)

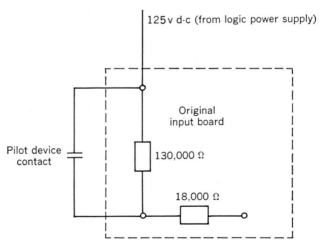

125 v d-c (from logic power supply)

Original
input board

Pilot device
contact

130,000 Ω

18,000 Ω

Fig. 11-26 Original input board. (*General Electric Co.*)

across the 130,000-ohm resistor, and the output of the 18,000-ohm resistor is then fed into the signal coil of the logic element desired. The operation is as follows: If the pilot-device contact is open, approximately 1 milliampere is fed into the signal coil by the output of a logic element. When the contact closes, the 130,000-ohm resistor is shorted out and approximately 8 milliamperes of current is fed into the signal coil by the output of a logic element, which approximates the ON current of the

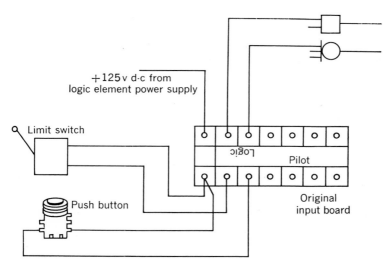

Fig. 11-27   Typical connections to original input boards. (*General Electric Co.*)

logic element. In this manner, the original inputs produce the same electrical characteristics that would be produced if the logic element were feeding information instead. The limit switch or pilot-device contact closes in on approximately 125 volts d-c, which is sufficient to break down films, dirt, and oxides which may appear on the contact surfaces, thus assuring reliable operation of the contact.

The original input resistor-divider networks are furnished on terminal strips called *original input boards*. The standard original input board has a capacity for six original inputs. It is so arranged that the wireman merely takes both sides of the limit switch, and hooks one side to the 125-volt d-c supply bus and the other side to a pilot-device terminal. A wire is then connected from the logic side of the terminal board to the logic element input, as shown in Fig. 11-27.

There are some special cases where alternating current must be put across the pilot-device contact, for example, when a number of limit switches are in series and pilot-light indication is desired as successive limit switches close down the line. At the end of the line of limit switches, a logic function is required. In these instances an a-c original input is required which can convert the a-c power into a d-c signal suitable for operating a logic element. A-c original inputs are available as boards, similar to the d-c original input boards, or packaged in a logic element plug-in can which can be inserted into a standard logic element receptacle. Each a-c original input board contains four a-c original inputs, and the a-c original input plug-in can contains three a-c original inputs.

11-5   Westinghouse Cypak Magnetic Control *

The operation of Cypak elements is based primarily on magnetic amplifier principles, but with the addition of the unique Ramey circuit. The following is a brief explanation of the operation of magnetic Cypak elements.

Figure 11-28 shows the familiar hysteresis loop, or B-H curve, for typical transformer steel. Because of the wide loop width, lack of squareness, and lack of sharp saturation point, this type of steel would not be suitable for use in magnetic amplifiers. With the development of grain-oriented magnetic alloys, however, the ideal, approximately square, hysteresis loop required for self-saturating operation became a reality. Figure 11-29 shows the B-H curve for Hipernik V, an alloy of approximately 50 per cent nickel and 50 per cent iron. It is evident that with only a slight change in H, it is possible to get a great change in B.

If this magnetic material is used in the circuit shown in Fig. 11-30 and a-c voltage E_G is applied, exciting current I_G will flow through the coil when terminal A is positive. With

* Reprinted with permission of the Westinghouse Electric Corporation.

proper values of E_G and N (turns of the coil), I_G will be just sufficient to drive the core to saturation during this positive half cycle. In the next negative half cycle, the rectifier pre-

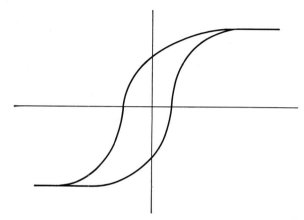

Fig. 11-28 Typical *B-H* curve of transformer steel. (*Westinghouse Electric Corp.*)

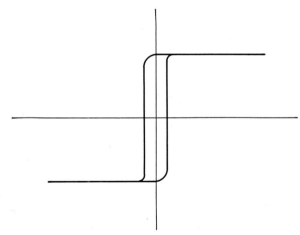

Fig. 11-29 *B-H* curve of Hipernik V. (*Westinghouse Electric Corp.*)

vents flow of current, so that, at the start of the next positive half cycle, the core remains saturated. Since the core cannot absorb any more voltage, there will be a voltage across the load R.   This output of the system is not, however, a controlled output.

The development of the Ramey circuit (Fig. 11-31) provided a fast-response magnetic amplifier by the addition of a reset circuit.   A second winding of N_R turns is added to the

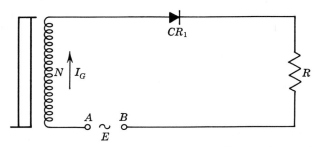

Fig. 11-30   Self-saturating circuit. (*Westinghouse Electric Corp.*)

magnetic core, and a resistor R_R is added such that E_R will drive the core to saturation during one-half cycle.   The rectifier $CR2$ and the polarity of E_R are arranged, however, so that the second winding will drive the core to negative saturation during the half cycle that current flows.

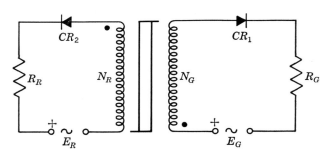

Fig. 11-31   Basic Ramey circuit. (*Westinghouse Electric Corp.*)

During the first half cycle, called the *gating* half cycle, the voltage E_G drives the core to positive saturation.   During this half cycle, the flow of current in N_R is blocked by the rectifier $CR2$ in this circuit (called the *reset* circuit).   During the next half cycle, current in the gate circuit is blocked by the rectifier $CR1$, but voltage E_R in the reset circuit drives the core to negative saturation. With continued application of E_G and E_R, the core will oscillate between positive and negative saturation, and there will be virtually no output to the load.

The output of this system can be controlled. If the reset voltage E_R is absent for one reset half cycle, an output will appear across the load resistance on the next gating half cycle because the core will remain saturated. A problem arises in finding the best way to prevent reset where an output from the circuit is desired. It is desirable that the circuit be driven by a voltage from other similar circuits. A simple solution is to place a relatively low resistance in series with the reset

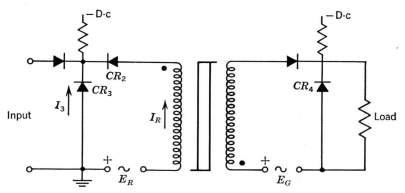

Fig. 11-32   One-input AND circuit. (*Westinghouse Electric Corp.*)

voltage. Then by supplying a voltage of proper polarity and sufficient magnitude across the resistor from some other source, block out the reset voltage. The proper value of resistance is a compromise between two conflicting requirements:

1. Low impedance in series with the reset voltage in order to reset completely with the voltage E_R

2. High impedance to provide least loading of the preceding or driving stage and show some gain per stage

This problem is solved by using the circuit shown in Fig. 11-32. Bias d-c voltages have been introduced in both gating and reset circuits. In the reset circuit, d-c (half-wave is adequate) is applied so that I_3, the current through rectifier $CR3$, is larger than I_R. Consequently, $CR3$ presents a low impedance to I_R, which flows through it and accomplishes reset of the core.

When an input voltage greater than E_R is applied, the current in rectifier $CR3$ tends to drop to zero, and the effective impedance of $CR3$ becomes its backward resistance, a very high value. Rectifiers $CR2$ and $CR3$ are blocked, reset current cannot flow, and an output appears across the load on the next half cycle. This circuit provides a one-input AND element; that is, an input to the element will produce an output.

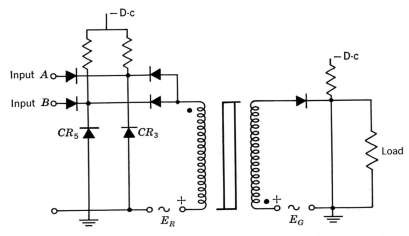

Fig. 11-33 Two-input AND circuit. (*Westinghouse Electric Corp.*)

The function of the d-c bias in the gate circuit is to reduce the output to the load resulting from core exciting current. $CR4$ presents a low impedance to exciting current, but a high impedance when the circuit is producing an output.

In the two-input AND circuit shown in Fig. 11-33, it can be seen that rectifiers and d-c bias voltage are provided for each of the input circuits. It is apparent that both inputs are required to develop an output. If either of the inputs is not present, reset of the core will be accomplished through the biased rectifier ($CR3$ or $CR5$).

Figure 11-34 shows a three-input OR circuit, which produces an output when there is an input to any one or more of the

input terminals.   The rectifiers $CR1$, $CR2$, and $CR3$ are introduced to provide isolation of the input signals.

The Cypak NOT circuit is very similar to the one-input AND
circuit. E_R is eliminated, and the terminals normally used

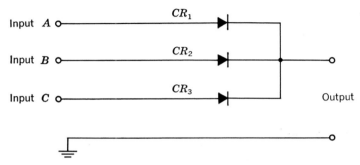

Fig. 11-34   Three-input OR circuit. (*Westinghouse Electric Corp.*)

for E_R are used as the terminals to the element, as shown in
Fig. 11-35.

The Cypak MEMORY circuit is essentially an information
storage device.   An input applied at the ON terminal develops

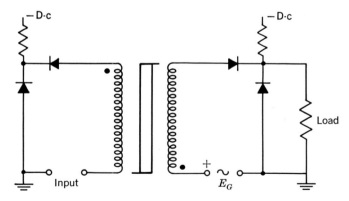

Fig. 11-35   Basic NOT circuit. (*Westinghouse Electric Corp.*)

a known output condition, which continues even though the
input signal is removed.   If an OFF signal is now applied at the
other terminal, the circuit switches to a different output condition and remains in that condition until an ON signal appears.

Two OR circuits are combined with two NOT circuits to provide the MEMORY function, as shown in Fig. 11-36.

If we assume that NOT circuit 1 is producing an output, this output resets the core in NOT circuit 2 through OR circuit 2. A half cycle later, NOT circuit 2 produces no output. Thus, NOT circuit 1 again resets core 2, with the result that this stable output condition is self-sustaining. The output is a half-wave voltage in phase with the supply voltage to NOT circuit 1.

A voltage of proper phase and magnitude applied to input 1 will reset core 1 through OR circuit 1. A half cycle later, no output appears from NOT circuit 1. Since core 2 is not reset,

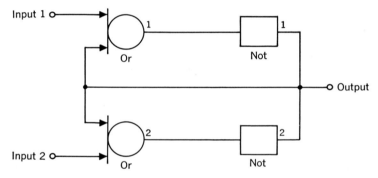

Fig. 11-36   Basic memory circuit. (*Westinghouse Electric Corp.*)

a half cycle later, an output results which is opposite in phase to the previous output. This output resets core 1 so that it will have no output on its gating half cycle. Even though the input is removed, the output remains stable in this condition. The output is shifted back to the original phase by introducing a voltage of proper phase and magnitude to input 2.

The storage of information is indefinite if the power-supply voltages are not interrupted. Statistically, there is a great likelihood that the stable state existing before a supply-voltage removal will be present after the voltage is reapplied. The condition which will cause loss of the stable state occurs when the core normally being reset by the stable output of the other core has its supply voltage interrupted at the end of its gating half cycle and the voltage is reapplied with polarities such that the gating half is repeated. Since the core was not reset during the interim, an output will occur. This output resets the other core, which was normally saturated. Therefore, the output shifts from its former stable state to the other stable state, just as if an input signal had been applied to effect the shift. This loss of stability occurs only if the input signal has been removed.

On applications where it is essential that a MEMORY circuit remembers its previous state, regardless of power-supply interruptions, an additional circuit may be included. This is termed a *retentive memory* unit and operates in connection with the MEMORY circuit shown in Fig. 11-36.

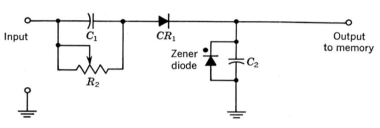

Fig. 11-37 Time-delay circuit. (*Westinghouse Electric Corp.*)

Proper system operation frequently calls for a delay period between the time when an input signal is received and the time that an output is produced. This result is obtained by the addition of a time-delay element to a MEMORY circuit. Figure 11-37 shows only the delay element, which feeds its output into input 1 of the MEMORY circuit (see Fig. 11-36).

The time constant C_1R_2 is short, a few cycles of the supply frequency at most. The time constant of C_2 and its load in the MEMORY circuit is long, about the same magnitude as the desired delay from the complete circuit. C_1 has very small capacitance compared with C_2. Therefore, applications of a pulse to the input will divide the input voltage across the capacitors as the reciprocal of their capacitances, respectively, with nearly all the voltage across C_1 and very little across C_2. During the portion of the cycle where the input is zero, C_1 discharges through R_2.   This discharge takes place independently of the rest of the circuit.

The second pulse input repeats the preceding operation, except that the pulse amplitude is reduced by the amount of charge present on C_1 and C_2.   As the pulse train continues, the charge on C_2 is slowly increased until sufficient current through terminal 1 changes the output state of the MEMORY circuit.

Fig. 11-38   Cypak logic power supply. (*Westinghouse Electric Corp.*)

The charge on C_2 will continue to build toward the peak value of the input pulse after the delay has elapsed, even though further increase in voltage has no effect on the output condition.   Since this build-up in voltage results in a higher capacitor voltage rating than actually necessary to operate the circuit, a Zener diode is added to hold the peak voltage to a preset value.   As the capacitor charge tends to exceed 6 volts, a discharge current will pass through the Zener diode, restoring it to the 6-volt level.

Discharge of C_2 occurs when the input voltage is removed and a resetting signal is applied to the MEMORY.   As in the case of the MEMORY circuit alone, simultaneous presentation of both inputs results in a zero output. A resetting voltage applied at the time-delay reset terminal immediately drops the voltage output to zero, even though C_2 has not yet discharged completely.

Operation of Cypak elements in most cases requires several a-c and d-c voltages for proper operation. For example, a

Fig. 11-39 Cypak element before sealing in can. (*Westinghouse Electric Corp.*)

two-input AND unit requires a-c voltages E_R and E_G and two d-c bias voltages. These voltages are as follows:

E_R = 8 volts a-c

E_G = 15 volts a-c

Bias = 23 volts d-c

These voltages are conveniently provided by the Cypak logic power supply (Fig. 11-38). This power-supply unit has adequate capacity to supply the requirements of about 150

Fig. 11-40 Cypak power channel and elements. (*Westinghouse Electric Corp.*)

Cypak logic blocks. A typical Cypak unit before sealing in polyester plastic is shown in Fig. 11-39. The Cypak power channel and completed Cypak elements are shown in Fig. 11-40.

SUMMARY

We have considered two systems for providing static control adaptable to almost any control circuit need. The two systems are basically similar and yet are individually different in their approach. The first system we considered (General Electric Static Control) uses magnetic amplifiers as the basic component. It should be noted that in this system, direct current is used in the gating and reset windings of the magnetic amplifier devices. This produces a d-c output which is not sensitive to differences in phase. Thus, phasing is not a problem in the design of the circuit using these units.

The second system we considered is that of the Westinghouse Electric Corporation manufactured under the trade name of Cypak. This system also uses the magnetic amplifier as its basic component. The approach is somewhat different, however, in that an a-c voltage is used for gating and reset. This produces an a-c output from the logic element and involves a 180° phase shift through each logic element. When designing a control circuit using this type of development, careful attention must be given to phase relationships so that the elements may function properly in the circuit.

REVIEW QUESTIONS

1. With magnetic amplifiers, what is the purpose of the gate winding?
2. With magnetic amplifiers, what is the purpose of the reset winding?
3. The load is connected in series with the _____ winding.
4. The General Electric Company static control elements use a _____ voltage input and produce a _____ voltage output. (a-c, d-c)
5. The Westinghouse Cypak elements use _____ voltage for their inputs and produce _____ voltage in their outputs. (a-c, d-c)

6. In magnetic amplifier logic elements, the signal voltage is used to overcome the _____ voltage in order to produce an output.

7. The core material used in magnetic amplifier logic elements is called _____ loop core material.

8. What is the purpose of the feedback winding on General Electric logic elements?

9. What is a Zener diode?

10. The basic circuit of the Westinghouse Cypak control is one known as the _____ circuit.

11. Draw a diagram of the typical hysteresis $B\text{-}H$ curve and the diagram for square-loop hysteresis curve.

12. Square-loop magnetic core material is made from a combination of iron and _____.

13. Draw the circuit for a three-input OR element using diodes as the principle component.

12

Transistors
as Logic Elements

The third system we shall discuss is one employing transistors and diodes as logic elements. The following information has been furnished by Southwestern Industrial Electronics Company of Houston, Texas, a leader in the field of transistor logic circuitry.

12-1 Transistors

The transistor is the latest and newest of the relaylike control devices. Invented in 1948, the transistor today is mechanically rugged, compact, cheap, and long-lived. The power-handling ability is at present limited to approximately 500 watts, with 5 or 50 watts the common limit. Operation is very fast, comparable in speed for our purposes with vacuum tubes. Currently available transistors will handle 20 to 50 volts and new ones up to 450 volts. Hence, the logic part of a transistor control circuit uses transistors, but the final closure of the power circuit to the motor must be accomplished by means of a relay or contactor.

In order that the student may better understand the logic circuits presented later, some basic facts concerning transistors and the proper handling of them will be discussed. Figure 12-1 shows some typical present-day transistors. The two on the left are small-signal types. These have a typical maximum voltage of 20 to 50 volts, and a maximum power rating of approximately $\frac{1}{20}$ to $\frac{1}{5}$ watt. Hundreds of type numbers exist, each with some characteristic making it especially suitable for some particular position in a radio set, computer, or other device. For our purposes, however, they are all basically very similar.

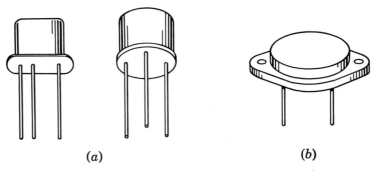

(a)   (b)

Fig. 12-1   Typical transistor shapes. (a) Small-signal type. (b) Power type. (*Southwestern Industrial Electronics* Co.)

The larger unit on the right is a typical power transistor. Again, there are many type numbers. Typical ratings are: maximum voltage, 20 to 80 volts; maximum power, 10 watts; maximum current, 2 to 10 amperes. The reason for the heavy flanged metal base is to permit bolting the transistor solidly to a metal plate (called a *heat sink*) or to a metal cabinet wall to help conduct away the heat generated in operation. Transistors are sensitive to temperature and are damaged by excessive heat.

Let us consider for a moment the internal construction and action of transistors. Figure 12-2 shows a simplified cross-section diagram of the internal construction of one common type of transistor. It consists of a thin slice of the rare metal germanium, with a spot of another metal such as indium melted on each side. The pellets of indium, known as the *dropping material,* are carefully heated so that the indium atoms diffuse into the germanium a precise distance. The process is very critical, since the thickness of the germanium base is only a few thousandths of an inch. Moreover, the materials must be extremely pure.

In the complete transistor, the action is such that a small control current applied between the base and emitter will cause a much larger current to flow between the emitter and

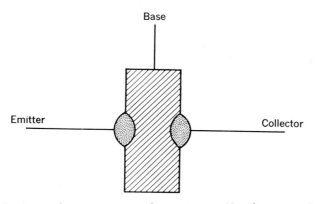

Fig. 12-2 Internal construction of transistor. (*Southwestern Industrial Electronics* Co.)

collector. The current gain is usually between 10 and 100. Thus, a small amount of power can control a larger amount of power. This construction is the so-called *junction* transistor. There is another construction known as *point-contact,* which is now obsolete. The symbols generally used on diagrams are, however, more reminiscent of the point-contact construction. Figure 12-3 shows the common transistor symbol in various forms. Emitter, base, and collector are labeled *E, B,* and *C* throughout. The symbol may be drawn right- or left-handed, upright or inverted, and it may or may not have a circle drawn around it. Figure 12-4 shows pin connections widely used on current transistors.

Transistors are made in two polarities, commonly referred

to as PNP and NPN, after the nature of the layers of material in the "sandwich" (Fig. 12-2). In the PNP type, the collector voltage must be negative with respect to the emitter. In the NPN type, the collector voltage must be positive with respect to the emitter. It should be noted that the middle letter of the designation indicates the collector polarity. In order for the transistor to conduct, the base-to-emitter polarity must be the same as the base-to-collector polarity. With a

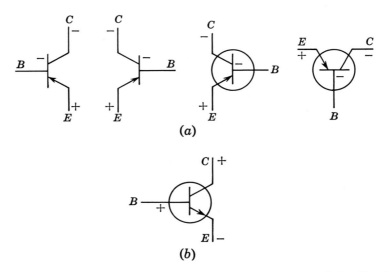

(a)

(b)

Fig. 12-3   (a) PNP transistor symbols. (b) NPN transistor symbols. (Southwestern Industrial Electronics Co.)

PNP transistor, the base polarity must be negative in order for the transistor to conduct. Positive base polarity will cause the transistor to cut off, or cease conduction.

The symbol for a PNP transistor (Fig. 12-3a) shows the emitter arrowhead pointing toward the base. Figure 12-3b shows the symbol for an NPN transistor. This symbol is different in that the emitter arrowhead points away from the base. The variations in position, the circle, etc., are the same as those for the PNP transistor. In order for collector current to flow in the NPN transistor, the base must be positive in

respect to the emitter.   Reverse polarity will cause cutoff of
the collector current.

A transistor is so rugged mechanically that it can be thrown
against a brick wall without damage.   Life-test evidence shows
that a good transistor in a correctly designed circuit will operate continuously for many years without any deterioration.

Every electrical component requires care, however.   Tubes
are mechanically fragile, and relays are sensitive to wear and
dirt.   Transistors are sensitive to certain wrong conditions,
too.   These are discussed in some detail below to show the

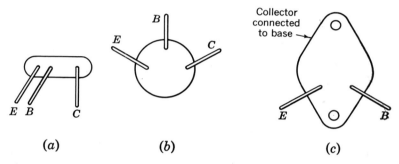

(a)   *(b)*   *(c)*

Fig. 12-4   Base connections of typical transistors (bottom view). (a) Small
flat case. (b) JETEC, or TO-9, case. (c) Power type. (*Southwestern Industrial Electronics Co.*)

types of difficulty possible because of errors in design or wiring
and to assist in trouble shooting.

Transistors can be ruined by certain incorrect electrical conditions.   These are:

1. *Overvoltage.*   Voltage overratings applied to the collector for even an instant can cause "punch through" and ruin
the transistor.

2. *High temperature.*   About 160° Fahrenheit (71° Centi-
grade) is about the limit for germanium transistors.   This is
a lower maximum temperature than for most other electrical
components.   Silicon transistors, where pure silicon metal is
substituted for the germanium, will stand higher temperatures.
Any germanium transistor that feels uncomfortably hot to
the touch is probably in trouble.

3. *Wrong polarity of collector voltage.* A transistor looks almost like a short circuit to voltage of the wrong polarity, so that heavy current can flow, causing overheating and failure of the transistor.

There is nothing in the transistor type number designation system (for example, 2N43, 2N169, 2N497) that gives any clue to whether the unit is PNP or NPN or gives any other of the transistor characteristics. Hence, one type must never be substituted for another without definite knowledge that it is a proper replacement.

Small transistors come from the factory with wire leads approximately 1½ inches long. When these transistors are mounted, the leads may be cut short (about ¼ inch) and the transistor plugged into a small socket, or they may be left longer and soldered directly into the circuit. When replacing a soldered transistor, always leave the wire leads as long as practical and solder them quickly with a clean, hot iron. This will prevent excessive heat from flowing along the wire and into the transistor body. The longer the wire and the shorter the time that the iron is applied, the fewer calories of heat will be conducted into the transistor. Soldering works fine if done with a little skill. On the other hand, many transistors have been overheated internally and ruined by cutting the leads short and then applying a dirty or too cool soldering iron for too long a time.

When replacing a power transistor, remember that it is attached to a metal plate or extrusion (heat sink) to help carry away the heat generated in operation. The mating metal surfaces must be free from dirt and the screws tightened up snugly. Some power transistors are mounted with a thin sheet of mica to insulate the case electrically from the heat sink. When using this type of mounting, you must be careful that there are no filings or dirt that could cut through the mica and cause a short circuit.

12-2   Transistor Circuits

Before considering transistors in logic circuits, let us consider some elementary transistor circuitry. Figure 12-5a shows the simplest transistor circuit. Voltage between the emitter and collector is supplied by a battery (or any other d-c power source). An ammeter is connected to read collector current. The base is connected through a switch SW and a resistor R to another battery B_2. The purpose of resistor R is to limit the flow of current through the base to a safe value, normally a few milliamperes or less. The polarity of the base supply voltage must be as shown. When the switch is open, no current will flow in the base circuit, and the collector (and load) current will be small, or almost zero. When the switch is closed, a current of approximately 1 milliampere will flow in the base circuit. When this happens, the amplifying action of the transistor will cause a much larger current to flow in the collector circuit (10 to 100 times as much). Suppose base battery B_2 is 10 volts and R is 10,000 ohms. When the switch is closed, approximately 1 milliampere will flow in the base circuit, and the transistor action will cause 10 to 100 milliamperes to flow in the collector circuit. The transistor is said to be operating in the *switching mode*.

When the base of a transistor is not connected to anything (is floating), the collector current will not be zero. There is always a little electric leakage, or conduction, between the collector and base. This is indicated in Fig. 12-5b as a resistance in dotted lines.

This leakage current increases drastically with increasing temperature. Thus, a transistor with collector voltage applied and the base open or floating will draw a little collector current because of the leakage. Under these conditions, the transistor will warm up a little, perhaps enough to increase the current considerably. The temperature will then increase further, causing more leakage and more current, etc., until the current rises to the point where the transistor is ruined. This condition is known as *thermal runaway*. A transistor destroyed in this manner may get hot enough to burn the paint off the case or even to melt the collector lead. Circuits are therefore designed so that the base is always connected to a point of definite voltage through an adequately low resistance and never left floating. Figure 12-5c shows a practical method of turning a transistor on and off. For the ON condition, the switch is up, connecting the base through resistance R to the -10-volt battery. For the OFF condition, the switch is down. The base is now connected through resistance R to a $+5$-volt battery. This gives a reverse bias and holds the base away from conduction, or biased off in a safe and definite manner.

Let us now consider what happens when a resistance is connected in the collector circuit (Fig. 12-6a). Switch the base to the 5-volt bus; the transistor is cut off. No collector current flows through load resistor R. The voltmeter reads the same as a supply voltage, 20 volts. Now throw the switch to the -10-volt bus. The transistor tries to conduct considerable current. When the current rises to approximately 20 milliamperes, it can go no higher, because the load resistor R now has a 20-volt drop across it. The voltmeter now reads zero (actually, perhaps half a volt). There is no collector voltage left and the transistor, as it were, can no longer transist.

The result is a stable full-conduction condition. In addition, the transistor does not get very warm, because it is not dissipating very much power. The current through the transistor is high enough, but there is very little voltage drop across the transistor. Power is voltage times current, and the power is all being dissipated in the external resistor R.

12-3   Transistor Amplifier

In order to illustrate and understand bias and amplifier action in transistors, suppose we consider a simple one-stage transistor audio amplifier. Referring to Fig. 12-6b, we can take the same circuit with the resistance load, but return the base to an adjustable source of bias voltage. This adjustable source is a potentiometer P connected across a small 1.5-volt battery. We can now adjust P so that the transistor draws approximately 10 milliamperes, or about halfway between zero and the maximum (20 milliamperes) that we have seen this circuit capable of passing. At this current, half of the 20-volt collector supply voltage will be dropped across the transistor and half across the load resistor R. The voltmeter V will read 10 volts. Under this operating condition, a small

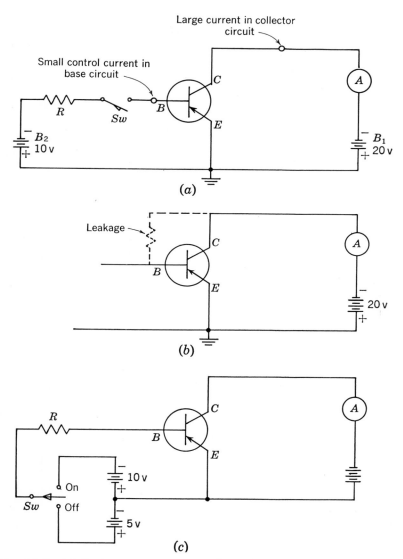

Fig. 12-5 (a) Basic transistor circuit. (b) Leakage current in transistors.
(c) Basic transistor switching circuit. (*Southwestern Industrial Electronics*
Co.)

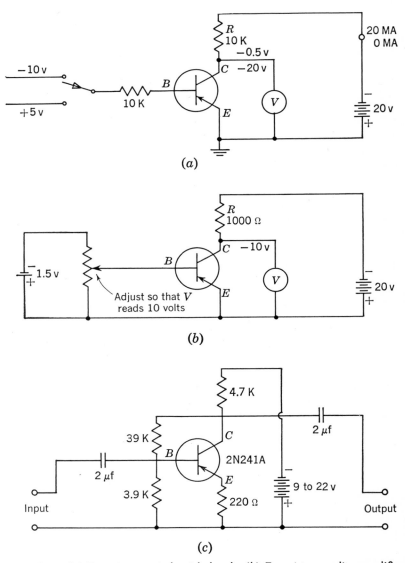

Fig. 12-6 (a) Transistor switch with load. (b) Transistor audio amplifier basic circuit. (c) Practical transistor audio amplifier. (*Southwestern Industrial Electronics Co.*)

change in bias voltage will produce a large change in collector voltage. Practically, if we adjust the potentiometer P
slightly to give a change in bias voltage of approximately 0.1
volt, the collector voltage V will change 50 times as much as
the bias voltage (1 to 5 volts). This mode of operation is
called *amplification,* or *class A operation,* as contrasted with
the switching mode which we have been considering.

A simple amplifier circuit such as shown in Fig. 12-6b is
not practical because the adjustment of bias is extremely critical and changes with different individual transistors and with
temperature. Also, there is no convenient provision for feeding signals in and out of the circuit.

Figure 12-6c shows a practical amplifier stage as used in
commercial instrumentation and audio equipment. The base
bias is taken from the collector supply. The various resistors
are connected in a stabilized bias circuit, which requires no
adjustment for ordinary variations in production transistors.
Signals are fed in and out through capacitors as shown. The
test for proper operating conditions is simply to measure the
collector-to-emitter voltage with a high-resistance voltmeter.
It should be approximately half of the supply voltage (within
30 per cent). If adjustment is required, the 39,000-ohm
resistor can be changed over the range of 15,000 to 100,000
ohms.

12-4   Transistor Logic Circuits

Let us now consider the transistor in some possible logic
circuits. There are many ways to connect transistors to produce AND, OR, and other logic elements. In all cases, transistors
in logic elements are used in the switching mode. Figure 12-7
shows an OR circuit using two transistors in parallel. When
either input 1 is ON or input 2 is ON, the output will be ON.
The definitions of ON are given on the diagram.

Since we are dealing with logic, which is a branch of
mathematics, we can start with any definitions we please, as a
mathematician does. The reasoning that follows after these
definitions must, however, be consistent or logical at all times.

In Fig. 12-7, when both inputs are OFF, both transistors

are biased off with 5 volts and are nonconducting.   There will be no current through the load resistors R, so the output voltage will be the same as the collector supply voltage, or -20 volts.   This condition is the one we have defined as being OFF. Now if input 1 is turned ON, transistor $TR1$ will conduct and the output voltage will drop to practically zero.   This is the condition we have defined as ON.   This is the same condition explained in connection with Fig. 12-6a.

If now we close input 2, transistor $TR2$ will try to draw current, but there is no collector voltage left for it to use, so the

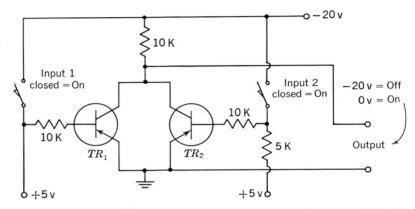

Fig. 12-7   Two-input two-transistor OR circuit. (*Southwestern Industrial Electronics Co.*)

output voltage will stay practically where it is (nearly zero). In other words, turning input 1 on will turn the output on. Similarly, turning input 2 on will turn the output on, and input 1 can then have no effect.   Thus either input 1 or input 2 can control the output.

Figure 12-8 is a parallel transistor AND circuit.   Here output ON is defined as -20 volts, when both transistors are nonconducting.   OFF is defined as having both transistors conducting and the output voltage near zero.   If we close input 1, transistor $TR1$ will be cut off, but transistor $TR2$ will still conduct enough to keep the output voltage near zero.   A similar condition exists if we close only input 2.   Both inputs 1 and

2 must be closed before the output voltage can rise to approximately 20 volts, the ON condition.

Any of these circuits may use three or more transistors instead of just two. When more than two transistors are used, it provides more than two inputs for the OR or the AND circuit.

There are methods which will allow the use of a single transistor to produce multiple-input AND and OR circuits. Figure 12-9 shows a single transistor OR circuit with three inputs. Output OFF is with the transistor fully conducting. If one of the inputs is turned ON, the transistor is cut off and the output

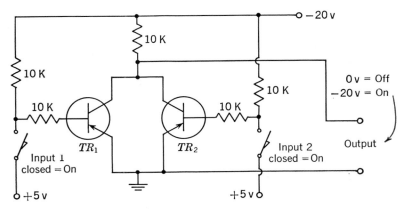

Fig. 12-8   Two-input two-transistor AND circuit. (*Southwestern Industrial Electronics* Co.)

voltage is −20 volts. This is the ON condition. If more inputs are closed, they have no effect, since the transistor is already cut off and nonconducting. Either input 1 or 2 or 3 will move the output to the ON condition.

If we were to define our terms the opposite way, we would have an AND circuit (Fig. 12-10). Here input ON means opening the switch. So long as any of the switches is closed, the transistor remains cut off and the output is 20 volts, or OFF. All the inputs, 1, 2, and 3, must be ON before the transistor can go to its conducting condition (zero volts).

Since the development work done to date in logic circuitry using transistors has been primarily custom design and construction of complete control systems, there has been very little standardization of the transistor logic circuitry. In custom design and engineering work, the logic element is generally designed to best perform the circuit function in the individual piece of equipment.

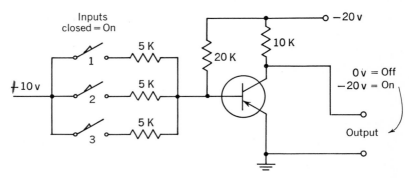

Fig. 12-9   Three-input single-transistor OR circuit. (*Southwestern Industrial Electronics Co.*)

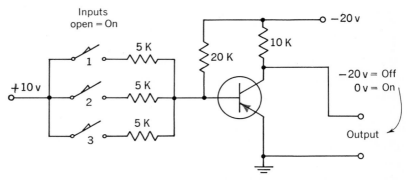

Fig. 12-10   Three-input single-transistor AND circuit. (*Southwestern Industrial Electronics Co.*)

The design of each logic element can be varied to give the desired output in order to provide the necessary input for the following element; that is, in one case it may be desirable to have ON be 0 volts and in another case −20 volts. The desired number of inputs will also cause a change in our design of individual logic elements.

Figure 12-11 is a control panel using transistor logic elements for the complete automated control of a central refrigeration system. This unit was designed and constructed by South-

Fig. 12-11   Logic circuit control panel. Large relays are for manual operation of system. (*Southwestern Industrial Electronics* Co.)

western Industrial Electronics Company and installed by the author. Measuring only 30 by 24 by 8 inches, this unit provides completely automatic start-up, shutdown, and load pro-

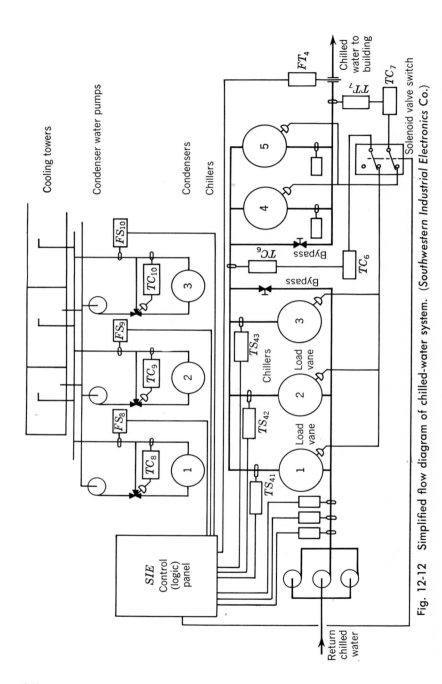

Fig. 12-12 Simplified flow diagram of chilled-water system. (*Southwestern Industrial Electronics Co.*)

240

portioning for five 500-ton compressor units and their associated pumps and valves. Figure 12-12 shows the five air-
conditioning compressors and their associated equipment in a
simplified flow diagram.

To illustrate further the use of transistors and diodes as
found in logic circuitry, Fig. 12-13 is a typical small replace-
able module on which the transistor logic elements are built.

Fig. 12-13 Typical subassembly module showing components. (Southwestern Industrial Electronics Co.)

Figure 12-14 shows the individual modules mounted on swinging racks for easy installation and accessibility in service.

Figure 12-15 shows the SIE Simarc dispatch console containing transistorized logic circuitry providing automatic remote control for an entire pipe-line system. This unit con-

Fig. 12-14 Modules assembled into racks. (*Southwestern Industrial Electronics* Co.)

tains 1,000 transistors and 1,200 diodes. The console provides automatic scheduling of periodic printout, display, and computation as required by the demands of the installation. It houses the push-button switches which enable dispatchers to direct remote operations and call for information from various points in the system, as needed.

The scheduling circuitry is arranged to cause readout of 100 alarm conditions throughout the system every 6 seconds, transmission of 50 data quantities every 30 seconds, and print-out of all system data every hour.

While such systems are possible with relay-type control circuits, it is obvious that the enormous space requirements to accommodate the thousands of relays which would be necessary will in many cases be prohibitive. Apart from this, how-

Fig. 12-15   SIE Simarc dispatch console. (*Southwestern Industrial Electronics* Co.)

ever, the chief advantage to solid-state logic elements is the lack of maintenance requirements because of the absence of moving parts such as those involved in relay circuitry.

SUMMARY

The third static control system we have considered is one using transistorized logic elements in custom-designed circuitry rather than standard components available as over-the-counter units. Freedom from the necessity for standardization allows the design engineer much more flexibility in achieving the desired results through variations in the individual logic circuits involved.

Since the transistor is in its infancy in comparison with the magnetic amplifier, it is the opinion of the author that further development of this component will lead to inexpensive standardized plug-in logic elements using the transistor and diode as its basic component.

REVIEW QUESTIONS

1. Draw the symbol for a PNP transistor.
2. Draw the symbol for an NPN transistor.
3. With a PNP transistor the base polarity must be _____ in respect to the collector.
4. With an NPN transistor the base must be _____ in respect to the collector to cause cutoff.
5. In transistor circuits the _____ voltage determines whether the transistor is normally conducting or normally cut off.

Index